THE
LAST
BEST
DIET
BOOK

THE LAST BEST DIET BOOK

Joyce A. Bockar, M.D.

STEIN AND DAY/*Publishers*/New York

First published in 1980
Copyright ©1980 by Joyce Bockar, M.D.
All rights reserved
Designed by Louis A. Ditizio
Printed in the United States of America
Stein and Day/*Publishers*/Scarborough House
Briarcliff Manor, N.Y. 10510

Library of Congress Cataloging in Publication Data
Bockar, Joyce A
  The last best diet book.

  1. Reducing diets—Anecdotes, facetiae,
satire, etc. 2. Obesity—Anecdotes, facetiae,
satire, etc. I. Title.
RM222.2.B589   613.2 '5   79-3710
ISBN 0-8128-2594-2

To my dear husband, Bob, who has seen me through thick and thin.

ACKNOWLEDGMENTS

I would like to thank Renni Brown for her help and encouragement in the production of this book, and my dear friend Ros for her unfailing support throughout several revisions of the manuscript.

CONTENTS

CONTENTS

Contents

INTRODUCTION

I think you should know a little about me and what gives me the right to write this book.

I am a fat-person. I was fat from early childhood until my mid-30s. I then lost 72 pounds—I went from 201 to 129, a weight I have now maintained for five years.

My mother tells me that I was fat by the time I was five years old. I can remember being taken to the "chubby" section of the store when I was ten or eleven. As a teenager, I generally weighed about ten times my age. From age fifteen to nineteen I gained 10 pounds a year, often dieting but never dieting successfully. From age twenty to twenty-four I hovered around the 180-pound mark, except for one loss, during medical school, of 36 pounds (every one of which I regained during my stint in the emergency room when I was an intern).

Over the years I had tried every conceivable diet, from safflower oil to grapefruit, from Stillman and Atkins to liquid protein, from Metrecal to Weight Watchers, and on through protein-sparing—you name it, I tried it.

I was able to lose weight, finally, because I found out why I hadn't been able to lose weight during all those years. I recognized, and to some extent solved, the unconscious problems that were keeping me fat. I also recognized some of the same problems in my overweight patients. I discovered that we fat-persons have reasons for being overweight. We are not just "pigs" or "slobs" who can't control our eating. We have unconscious reasons—powerful ones; powerful enough to undermine our every effort to lose weight.

We *can* do something about it. Once I had done something about it, once I myself was thin, I could afford to tell my obese patients that I had weighed 201 pounds and understood them and could help them lose weight as soon as they were ready and as soon as they had identified the unconscious determinants of their overweight. As I listened to these patients, certain themes seemed to recur. I have set these themes down in this book.

In so doing, I have given you the most common unconscious reasons for staying fat. If you identify with one or more of them, you are well on the way to robbing your unconscious of its power to keep you fat. If you do not identify with any of them you either have other reasons, which the process of self-discovery inherent in this book will help you recognize, or you have become fat from aging or lack of exercise and have simply found it difficult to diet. In this case you should find my special dieting methods very useful.

These methods take into account the behavior and psychology of overeating, which, after all, is something all fat people do. I have developed a way of dieting which allows "cheating" without undermining weight loss. This method will work only after you have at least recognized that there may be unconscious reasons for your overweight.

My dieting approach can be used with any legitimate diet (any diet that causes weight loss). It can also be used for maintenance—many of my patients have used it successfully, and I myself have used it successfully to maintain my goal weight for five years.

Introduction

My patients and I lost weight after we had dealt with, or at least recognized, our unconscious reasons for being fat. We kept it off by using my dieting methods. I went through this twofold process with a psychiatrist; my patients do it with me, their psychiatrist. You can do it with this book. If you do, it will truly be your last, best diet book.

THE LAST BEST DIET BOOK

CHAPTER 1

THE
BOTTOM
LINE

There are a few hundred diet books out on the market. We have all tried the diets in them, and we have all lost some weight on one or more of them. Somehow, we have either never been able to lose all the weight we wanted, or we have lost it and put it right back on. Somehow, we say, we can't stick to a diet. Somehow we never manage to "retrain our eating habits," that oh-so-desirable and, for us, oh-so-impossible goal set forth in most of these books.

Well, it seems obvious that, if we've all lost some weight on a mad variety of diets, the particular diet we go on doesn't make any difference so long as it has between 800 and 1,000 calories. That's right—if you count up the calories in any of the popular low-calorie diets, they have between 800 and 1,000 (or less than 800 for a starvation diet). (Fasting is not a diet.) The diet club regimens have 1,200 calories, which may be too many calories to allow some people to lose weight. Besides, it's slow losing on 1,200 calories.

The way in which diets that control carbohydrates rather than calories work, and don't work, will be discussed later in this book. For now, the point is it doesn't matter if the 800 to 1,000 calories are made up of all protein, some protein, all carbohydrates, or even all fat. That's right; you could lose weight eating two pieces of pie per day. That diet has about 800 calories, and if that's all you ate, you would lose about a pound a day for the first week or two.

The actual diet may not matter in terms of weight loss, as long as it has less than 1,000 calories; but what about nutrition? With unbalanced diets, you need vitamins and often mineral supplements. Balanced diets are easier to stay on — your body won't cry out for missing nutrients, and they're less boring — but you don't have the fun of losing very fast in the beginning. And what difference does it make *what* the diet is if you can't stick to it?

So, if diets don't count, what does? Psychology! Mental attitude, mental set, readiness to go on a diet, readiness to stay on a diet and, most of all, *readiness to be thin*, which means clearing your unconscious mind of the feelings and fears that have, for all these years, prevented you from losing weight and keeping it off.

But first, there's a mental attitude we have to face: nobody wants to diet, especially us. Nobody wants to limit their intake of food, and fat-persons, as I shall call us from time to time, attach more meaning to food than just physical survival. We need it to survive mentally! Or do we? If nobody wants to diet, then how do we, as fat-persons, do it? By what process do we get ourselves to diet, and *why* do we diet?

We all diet for a higher goal. We actually suppress, for a while, our most basic need and urge. What is that goal? Thinness, you say. Yes, but thinness brings many things to the minds of many people. Thinness itself has become a goal for those living in our society, which values thinness. People respect other people more if they are thin. Thinness means you are in control. You're not a fat slob. Unconsciously people think of fat people as out of control, disorganized, undisciplined, or stupid. Too often, fat people think of themselves that way too.

The higher goal for which we desperately control our eating varies with each person. It may be to get a mate, to get a better job, to be able to run or play tennis. In order to overcome the basic feeling of not wanting to diet, it's important that you decide what your higher goal is; that you decide what thinness will bring. As I shall show you later, it is very often the fantasies of what thinness will bring that stand in your way. Yes! On an unconscious level we very often fantasize things that prevent us from staying on a diet.

There are other things that prevent us from staying on a diet, including mental sets derived from previous experience. A mental set is the set of feelings you have toward an experience, based on your previous experience. One typical mental set is "I can't stay on a diet, period. I've tried a million diets and I can't stay on one." Others are: "I always put it back on"; "I'll never be thin"; "I can't resist a particular food."

We bring to a diet a whole host of defeatist attitudes. True, there are many unconscious reasons why we stay fat, but we still have to deal with our history. We still have to deal with the fact that up to now we have not been able to stay on a diet, and up to now we have never been able to keep weight off even if we *could* stay on a diet.

So how can we approach a diet differently? How can you know that this time will be different? I know that if you learn to approach yourself differently, you can approach a diet differently. By the end of this book you will know that, whatever diet you go on, you can lose weight and keep it off.

•   FAT-PERSONS   •

One of the first things we have to realize about ourselves is that, when it comes to our weight, we are sometimes dishonest.

We are often dishonest about our food intake, more frequently with ourselves than with other people, who aren't as likely to underestimate what we eat. ("I only had a little of this and a bit of that"; or, on a diet in which you have to weigh your food, you don't buy a scale and you figure that what really is eight ounces of hamburger is four ounces.)

We don't like to think of ourselves as different. We don't acknowledge that we are fat-persons. We keep on saying to ourselves, "I'm not *that* fat." We all have a concept of exactly what "that" fat is, a concept that varies according to what weight we are at the moment. When I weighed 180 I said to myself, "I'm not *that* fat." That fat would, at the time, have meant weighing 200 pounds. I eventually did weigh 200 pounds, but of course that didn't keep me from saying to myself, "I'm not *that* fat."

When you can say to yourself, "I *am* fat," and can say to yourself at the same time, "I hate it," without saying, "I hate myself," *then* you can go on a diet.

For the moment: What is fat? Or fatness? It is however overweight you are. It is how you feel about yourself. For most of us, if we feel fat, we *are* fat. For some normal-weight people and some underweight people, fat is a concept used to focus in on their terrible feelings about themselves. They don't say, "I am a terrible person," they say, "I am fat." But no amount of losing weight helps these people, who, in extreme cases, are diagnosed as having anorexia nervosa. For the rest of us, fatness is any amount you are over what you want to be.

Okay. So you've accepted the fact that you're fat. Have you? You know you are fat, but have you accepted it as part of yourself? Do you know that you may not be just fat, you may be a *fat-person*?

A fat-person is different from a not-ever-fat-person. A fat-person has a hard time stopping eating. By that I mean, did you ever leave one-half of anything you liked on a plate? Did you ever leave one-half of anything you didn't like on a plate? Did you ever leave any food on a plate if you weren't sick? Did you ever have one hors-d'oeuvre? Did you ever have one-half of a sandwich?

When we fat-persons start eating, we can't stop. Food makes us hungry! What should, after a while, be satiating often makes us want more. I always say that I am hungriest after a meal.

A fat-person thinks a lot about food. We think in terms of mealtimes. We think of how and where we are going to get our next meal. Taking a trip? Where do we stop for lunch? Do we take a no-frills flight to Florida? Never. Even though we can go three hours without food, we want the meal on the plane.

Fat-persons hate themselves. The feeling of self-hatred that we all have is indescribable, yet we all know what I mean. This self-hatred even causes us to eat more, perpetuating the whole cycle that we all know so well: "The more I eat the more I hate myself. The more I hate myself, the more I eat." So how do you break out of that? I will tell you in the next few chapters.

Fat-persons are unbelievably self-conscious. We are always conscious of that roll of fat called, euphemistically, the "midriff bulge." We are conscious of the position we are sitting or standing in. We are always, *always* conscious of the fact that we are fat. We are conscious of our thighs rubbing together — our pants get worn out there (male or female). We are conscious of the tightness of our clothes because we haven't accepted ourselves enough to buy clothes that fit; because we're always going to lose weight and we don't want to waste the money. Men, more than women, are conscious of their double chins. And don't you know we all have a nice face! "You have such a nice face. Why don't you lose some weight?" Such comments don't inspire us to lose weight. Instead, they inspire us, when in a social situation, to hope that our nice face will make up for our fat body.

Fat-persons are envious of all thin people, no matter what or who the people are. We are envious of their thinness. We are envious of the fact that they can control what they eat, or, worse, that they can eat what they want and never gain weight. We feel we can never eat what we want, *ever!* Much of this book will be devoted to the idea that you *can* eat what you want, as much as you want, for very short periods (such as two days), as soon as you've learned that you do have control over your weight. Ordinarily, on a diet, you don't even enjoy what you are allowed because you're too busy feeling deprived.

Fat-persons are "all-or-nothing" when it comes to eating. It is almost easier for us to eat nothing or very little than to limit our intake if everything is "allowed." Fat-persons, some fat-persons, never get full or can't tell when they're full unless they've consumed 8 pounds of food and water. Some of us can't even tell if we're hungry. I've met some fat-persons who are hungry all the time and some who say they never really feel hungry, who eat either out of habit or compulsively.

Fat-persons have a strange metabolism. We gain weight with astonishing ease. You know, most thin people don't gain or lose weight as easily as a fat-person can. If a fat-person and a regular-person eat the same 3,000-calorie meal, the fat-person may gain as much as 2 pounds and the thin-person nothing. This tendency, I am sorry to say, does not go away when we reach goal.

There are 40 million overweight Americans, many of whom are fat-persons. Fat-persons may inherit the tendency to be fat from their parents. This has never been proven, however, or disproven, for that matter. We certainly learn bad eating habits from our parents. What's worse, we learn to use food to assuage all painful and pleasant emotions. We were taught these things when we were too young to resist or protest, and now we are stuck with them, although we were not at fault.

It is not only from our parents that we learned to eat junk food. Our environment is loaded with food. Junk food and booze are used for social get-togethers; junk food is promoted on television, billboards, the radio. We even learn to eat junk food from our children, who succumb to T.V. sales. There is a restaurant on almost every city street. There is a pizza place in nearly every town; there is a McDonald's or a Burger King or a Kentucky Fried Chicken no more than five miles from just about anywhere. We are bombarded with food, especially junk food, and everybody can eat it but us!

Don't you really hate people who can eat whatever they want and don't gain weight? They can have cereal and pancakes for breakfast, a Big Mac for lunch (with fries and a milk shake), a large steak and salad with plenty of dressing for dinner (and apple pie with ice cream for dessert), and not gain weight. No wonder we hate them.

They really do have a different metabolism. Yes, a different metabolism. Everybody knows, as I said, that the same 3,000-calorie meal would result in little or no gain for a true thin-person and possibly a 1- or 2-pound gain for a fat-person. You tell me the gain is water? Then tell me what, metabolically, causes the fat-person to retain water while the thin-person excretes it. And further, tell me what metabolic process will keep that 2-pound gain on the fat-person's body unless the fat-person immediately starves it off.

I don't have the answers. All I know is that the books that say it takes 3,500 calories to gain 1 pound were written by thin people. Everybody knows we're different. It's so obvious that science hasn't taken the time or energy to prove it. Don't you hate people who can't eat a lot or who leave food on their plate every time they eat? (Food that you fantasize finishing, I might add.) Don't you hate people who look thin and order diet food? Don't hate them — they could be fat-persons. They might be you someday.

No, we can't help our genetically-inherited metabolism; nor can we help the learning that took place, or the extra fat cells that were built up in infancy. No, we can't help the deluge of food commercials on T.V.; nor can we help the plethora of places to eat that seem to flourish on every block in every town. But we can help ourselves! *And* we can eat all the food we want, sometimes!

We are not alone, and we are not entirely at fault.

Fat-persons have a long history of being fat. We may have been fat from early childhood, in which case we have a long history of being rejected by our peers, being teased, being called names like Fatty, Fatso, Elephant, Blob, Slob, or "pleasingly plump." We have a very long history of self-hatred. We may have been outgoing or shy, but the self-hatred remains.

What about the people who were not fat from childhood? Who got fat after pregnancy, or who found that they used to be able to eat whatever they wanted to until, with a small increase in age, they got fat when they continued to eat that way? Well, fat people become fat-persons after awhile. They have the same history of dieting failure, frustration, anger, and self-hatred, though they may have a better base of self-confidence than an all-his-or-her-life fat person. Fat people concentrate on food the same way fat-persons do; they experience the same social rejection and lack of respect. It's just that fat-persons have put up with it longer.

Fat people or fat-persons, the need is the same: to say to yourself (like an alcoholic admitting that he can't handle liquor), "I am a fat-person. I gain weight from eating a butterfly. My body can't handle food, but I can handle my body. More importantly, I can handle my mind!"

When I was discussing the difference between fat-persons and thin-persons with my thin-person husband, I asked him, "How do I differ from you?" He said, immediately, "You're more compulsive." We are all compulsive; compulsive eaters, certainly, but we also tend to be compulsive and perfectionistic in other areas. Many of us are compulsively neat or, for that matter, compulsively sloppy. Some of us have recurrent thoughts that we can't get out of our heads, and not only the ones about food.

We are perfectionists. Not only in our work, but especially in dieting. We are so perfectionistic about dieting that the moment we are not perfect on the diet we feel that we've blown it and we figure we might as well blow the rest of that day and maybe even the diet. (I have a simple method for curing *that* problem.)

The bottom line for fat-persons is the issue of control. As children we were completely controlled by our parents. Our parents fed us and told us what to do every step of the way. Sometimes the only thing under our control was our intake of food. If we wanted to please our mother, we ate, and if we were angry at our mother, we could do one of two things: not eat, which some children do, or eat too much as a way of showing that we had control over ourselves and were not subject to her control. We were swallowing the emotion of anger with a food chaser.

Many of us attempt to control others with our dieting. We may ask people not to serve certain things when we're there, or we may say that we can't do routine things because we're too weak, tired, or irritable from dieting. Many of us have asked other people—spouse, parents, children, friends—to help us diet, in effect, to control us because we can't control ourselves. ("You shouldn't let me eat that.")

Food is used as a reward, which is a form of control; and the withholding of food often is used as a punishment, which is certainly control. We tend to use food both as a reward for ourselves and as a punishment. We punish ourselves by overeating. In case you never thought of it that way, what is the desired result of punishment? Remorse and guilt, right? What do you feel after you've eaten something you shouldn't have? Remorse and guilt? Right!

When you feel guilty, you feel bad. You're no good. You punish yourself with food, bet on it. Worse, you punish yourself with food for having eaten food. You may not realize it; it just feels like you can't stop eating. Frankly, I don't think we can ever change this most ingrained habit of rewarding ourselves with food, celebrating things with food, even mourning things with food; but I have a concept that may help us deal with it.

I do think we can learn to stop punishing ourselves with food, stop feeling guilty when we eat, and enjoy eating again. *Nobody who is fat truly enjoys eating!* You may think that you're fat because you love food and you love to eat, but when you're fat there's too much guilt and too much self-hatred for you to truly enjoy eating. If you don't feel the self-hatred or the guilt, it may be unconscious, and it may be one of the things preventing you from losing weight.

•   FAT-PERSONS AND CONTROL   •

We would like to be in control of our eating, but we want to be in control of many other things too. We want to be in control of our mates, of our children, of relationships with friends, business associates, and parents. We fat-persons, whether we recognize it consciously or not, want to control just about everything. "No," you say. "That's not true. All I really want to control is my weight." I believe you, but examine your life. Who has control over whom in your life?

If you discover that you have very little control of the relationships in your life, maybe you are reverting to that childhood pattern: "All I can control is my own intake, and I will intake as much as I want." If you discover that you have very little control, you may realize that you really want more control but don't know how to get it. You don't know how to stick up for yourself (especially when you feel fat and ugly and you're afraid if you get "pushy" your mate will leave you or your friends will leave you).

If you discover, in examining your life, that you are in control of a great many relationships and situations, you may be eating because that's the only area in which you can "afford" to be out of control. If you are responsible for too many things, it is absolutely impossible to diet, and the anxiety involved in too many responsibilities becomes another cause of overeating.

Eating may be your only outlet, the only place where you can let yourself go. This is especially true if you have sexual hangups that keep you from letting yourself go in bed. Eating is often a substitute for sex. (Fat is often a way of avoiding sex, as I will explain later.)

● EATING OUT OF BOREDOM OR TO RELAX ●

We often eat out of boredom because we have nothing else to do; or, worse, we eat because it is our only real pleasure in life. Think about that. Is eating your only pleasure in life? Why? Your answer, whether you're married or not, is that you are lonesome, that you have little social life; or that you are alone most of the time, children or not, and you are stuck in the house.

Or you are stuck at work with the coffee and donuts, as I was. One part of my medical internship some years ago involved being in the emergency room from 8:00 P.M. to 8:00 A.M. for thirty days, with one day off. Now, the way the shifts go in hospitals, the nurses are on first shift from 3:00 P.M. to 11:00 P.M., on second shift from 11:00 P.M. to 7:00 A.M., and on third shift from 7:00 A.M. to 3:00 P.M. Those working from 11:00 P.M. to 7:00 A.M. are served dinner at 2:00 A.M. At 8:00 P.M., the start of my shift, the nurses were having coffee and donuts. I had coffee and donuts. At 11:00 P.M., the 3:00 P.M. to 11:00 P.M. nurses were having pizza. I had pizza. At 2:00 A.M. I went down to dinner. At 8:00 A.M. the 7:00 A.M. to 3:00 P.M. nurses were having coffee and donuts. I had coffee and donuts. Talk about being stuck at work!

The emergency room was a very tense place. We ate any time we could, for relaxation. I gained 30 pounds in thirty days. With that schedule, I didn't see much of my husband, except one hour per day from 7:00 P.M. to 8:00 P.M., during which time he *fed* me! I slept all day and worked all night — no sex — and eating became, temporarily, my only pleasure in life. If you're wondering whether or not I found pleasure in my work as a doctor, yes, I did. There's a great deal of gratification in literally saving people's lives, but there is also a great deal of tension and excitement involved, and every fat-person I know eats when tense or excited.

Don't make the mistake of thinking that a job in which you were busy enough would keep you from eating. It doesn't work that way. If you're a secretary, you are involved with the coffee wagon and going out to lunch. If you are an executive or have a job in which your hours are flexible, there is absolutely nothing to stop your eating. Men sometimes succeed in keeping busy on their lunch hour, only to come home tired and very hungry, which virtually guarantees their overeating at night.

Nor do vacations stop us from overeating. In fact, we eat more on vacations because we want to let go, go on a spree, relax. Who can diet on vacation? My answer is, don't. "But then I'll gain 10 or 15 pounds," you say. My answer is, "So what?" Once you have the knowledge that you have control over your weight, you can afford to gain weight and then immediately lose it again.

How do you get the knowledge that you can control your weight? It comes from doing what you'll learn how to do in this book. It comes from not being afraid to be thin, from understanding the unconscious motivations that are keeping you fat, and from finally dieting successfully all the way down to goal.

• SOME REMARKS ON DIETING •

Successful dieting is the most difficult thing you have done in your life or ever will do. If you think you've had some hard times with money, jobs, illness, the death of loved ones, children, school, moving, or getting rejected socially, they are *nothing* compared to successful dieting. Dieting is not only not easy, we all (we fat-persons) have to be on a diet the rest of our lives, sometimes. Even the death of a loved one is something you eventually get over and accept to some degree. Dieting goes on (intermittently) forever, and we can never accept it fully, yet we can live with it and work with it and keep ourselves thin! Forever!

How? What secret am I keeping? No secret. The secret lies within *you*. It lies in the particular unconscious motivations that are preventing you from losing weight. You're likely to find one or more of these in the next chapter, which deals with common unconscious motivations.

Yet what if, you say, you really don't have any unconscious reasons for not wanting to lose weight? You say you're fat because you love food, or because your age crept up on you, or from pregnancy or from lack of exercise, and you're really basically happy except for the fact that you're fat. If you're so happy, why are you fat? You say, it's hard to lose weight. I agree! But I suggest that if, for whatever reasons, you have been fat for more than two years, something is keeping you that way, and it isn't just that dieting is very difficult.

Many people, for example, who are fifty-five or over get fat because they think it doesn't matter any more. They are depressed, their sex drive has suffered, and they are in such long-established relationships that they don't care and they don't think their mates care; but if they didn't care, they wouldn't be reading this book. Each sex and age group has its particular reason for going on a diet. At all age groups, we think we diet to be more attractive to the opposite sex, but, as I will show you in the next few chapters, many of us have unconscious problems, fantasies, etc., involving the opposite sex which prevent us from losing weight.

In addition to unconscious motivations, we can be prevented from losing weight by psychological problems peculiar to dieting itself. As I mentioned, we all resent dieting. We walk around feeling deprived, angry, and irritable. We know, or think we know, it's for the rest of our lives, and this brings up all our anger at the world for demanding thinness. ("Why can't I be accepted for myself?") It brings up our anger at our parents for feeding us too much as babies and creating extra fat cells, our anger at ourselves for being unable to control our eating, our anger at people—our loved ones, our mates, boy friends and girl friends—for not accepting us as us.

Actually, they do accept us as us, but we tend to think of ourselves as our "personality" and our "face," so when they accept us, we think they are accepting us for just those two characteristics and forgetting about our bodies. When they make some comment about our weight, there is an explosion. They must be accepting us only for our personality and our face because, we think, they wouldn't accept us if they acknowledged to themselves that we were fat.

It is we, of course, who cannot accept our bodies, we who try to deny that our bodies exist, all the while being unbelievably self-conscious of them, we who think of ourselves as a face with a personality, we who don't accept ourselves. Our loved ones accept us, and they recognize the fat and love us anyway. Other people do not accept us as readily; we are rejected or passed over for promotions or subtly put down or not noticed.

Then there are the subtle and not-so-subtle comments: "Oh, you're on a diet *again*." "Think you'll make it this time?" "A friend of mine lost 60 pounds and he put it right back on again." And all the helpful advice: "Why don't you try X's diet? My girl friend lost 30 pounds in two months." I know, your friend may be trying to be helpful. But what does it say for what she thinks of your ability to choose a good diet? What does it say for what she thinks of your ability to lose weight?

I am not suggesting that every attempt at helping you is an attempt to control or manipulate you. If you ask someone what type of diet you should go on, then the comment is in order. If you announce that you're on a diet (which you definitely should not do, for reasons I'll explain in a moment), then you are inviting comments, and people will try to be helpful. (You see, they really do want you to feel better about yourself.)

• PEOPLE POWER •

Let's talk about why you shouldn't announce to people that you're on a diet. First, if you make an announcement to tell your family, your family feels obliged to help you diet while you're eating. Other people do too. The help takes many forms: "You shouldn't eat that." "I didn't think that was allowed on your diet." "You poor thing. Is that all you're allowed?" "What can you eat for dessert?"

Second, some of us are all too easily sucked into letting other people do our dieting for us. Announcing that you're on a diet not only brings forth those "helpful" comments, it actually gives power to *other* people. It gives them, they think, the right to watch what you're eating and to "help" you stop eating when *they* think you've had enough.

Did you ever notice thin-persons telling each other that they've eaten too much or informing each other of the caloric content of what they're eating? It is fat-persons who give other people, including our families, the power to judge us, to tell us whether we've been bad or good on our diet. This process strengthens our conscious or unconscious feelings that we can't control ourselves and are somehow inferior.

It's true that you can't very well completely conceal the fact that you're on a diet from your family. But you can field their well-intentioned comments by saying, "I eat what I eat. I know you love me, but I must do this myself," and *meaning* it—for doing it yourself is the only way it can be done permanently.

One of the characteristics of our society is that we want what we want when we want it. We can't wait. We especially can't wait for food—the tremendous boom in "fast-food" chains attests to that. The problem is that dieting is essentially a waiting game, waiting to get thin, and we are impatient. We believe that the whole world will be different when we're thin, and this belief, which to some extent is really true, makes the waiting even harder.

If you use the time you are dieting to find interests for yourself, to explore yourself, to learn a new job skill, to learn to get out of the house or stop working compulsively, you will feel less pressure from the waiting, mainly because you won't be just waiting and hoping: you'll be doing. Dieting involves other kinds of waiting besides waiting to get thin; it's waiting for the next meal or your only meal. It's waiting until the morning to weigh yourself. It's waiting for a respite from hunger.

This waiting somehow seems more acute when we're dieting because we are already dissatisfied with the meal we know is coming. If we know a satisfying meal is coming, it's easier to wait, but if it's a binge that's coming, we can't wait. Or can we?

I always ask my patients what they think will change when they get thin. Many say they won't be so shy; but they got fat because they were shy. So don't bet on losing your shyness with your weight. I think it is best to make a list for yourself of things you think will change if you become thin and things that probably won't. Do it now, and then do it again after you have read this book.

I must say that up to now I've said "we," "us," we "fat-persons," and so on, as if we were all alike. Obviously, we are not all alike just because we're all fat, but being fat and dieting without success imparts to all of us a certain common history and experience, a common history of emotions, of emotional experience, of our relationship to ourselves. Very few of us can hate being fat without hating ourselves, at least a little. All of us envy thin people. We can even envy a whore or a pimp who is thin. In fact, we envy anybody and everybody who is thin. Let's stop looking at everybody else and take a look at ourselves, our fantasies of being thin, and a myriad of other fantasies, desires, and fears—conscious and unconscious—that may be keeping us fat.

CHAPTER 2

YOUR
UNCONSCIOUS
PROBLEMS

• FOOD AND LOVE •

When we were very young, many of us were told to finish everything on our plates. In very many instances, we ate to please our mother. We ate for a reward of food, like ice cream or candy. We ate because our mother said it was a shame to waste food, either because "the children in Asia are starving" or because "I paid good money for that food, and you're not going to waste it."

Now, there are two things we are dealing with here. One is eating to please your parents when you are young; the other, often related, is wasting food. Many of us, unconsciously, are still eating to please our parents who, dead or alive, are now inside our heads. There is no doubt that in the present, as adults, many of us are still "forced" to eat by our parents. The unconscious reason for eating is that we will be a good girl or boy and we will be loved. No fat-person can doubt the equation of food with love! Some of us still want those parents inside our heads to love us, and so we eat.

The food we are eating represents our membership in the "Clean Plate Club." It represents love from our parents. It often represents the love that we didn't get — or feel we didn't get. It may now represent love from our mates, but that is a spin-off from the original equation of parental love and food. A good thing to ask yourself is, "Why do I want love from my parents now?" The answer is likely to come out something like this: "Because parents are supposed to love their children. I need their love."

My question is, "What do you need it for?" Nine times out of ten it wouldn't do you any good now. It's too late. Your feelings about yourself are already formed. Imagine how you would feel if your parents started loving you now, no matter what age you are. For one thing, you wouldn't believe them! You wouldn't know what to do with the love if you did believe them. Nothing would change if they started loving you now. You can't make up for the lost love, either with them or with food.

Does that realization make you feel sad or depressed? Well, it *is* sad. It has to be experienced, realized, mourned, and finally accepted. Yes, accepted, you can only "make up" for the lost love by finding love, not food, in the present! There is, of course, considerable question as to whether you can "make up" for the lost love at all in terms of the loss of self-esteem that occurs when one or both parents don't love you. Food and fatness, though, certainly don't make up for that lost self-esteem either. They aggravate it. As I said, if you feel you can never make up for the sadness of the love you see yourself as not having received from one or both parents, then accept that fact and divorce food from it. Food isn't going to make up for it either.

The problem here is that we seem to need external love for self-love. Certainly it's true that if your parents never loved you, you most likely don't love yourself, and you most likely feel that you are unlovable in a most basic sense. If you are fifteen or older and your parents never loved you, I hate to say this, but it's too late now. Even if they suddenly started loving you, both you and they could never make up for the loss of love, for the loss of self-esteem, for the inability to love yourself that you suffered as a result of their not loving you up to the age of ten or so.

How do you make up for the lost love? How do you make up for the inability to love yourself? Certainly not by eating food! Food is *not* love. Too much food only hurts your self-esteem, makes you less lovable to yourself and to others. If your parents didn't love you, or if they did and you seem to need to keep re-experiencing that love in ways that are no longer possible, food won't help you now.

We all seem to need to believe that our parents love us, because if they love us, then we are lovable. That was true when we were children, but it is not true now. We can become lovable even if we don't think we are now. Some of us who got fat later— after the age of twenty—do not feel that we are basically unlovable (unworthy of being loved) by our parents. Instead, we feel we are basically unlovable to our mates or to people in general. Obviously, one of the ways you can become lovable to yourself is by dieting down to goal. If you are lonely, and no one loves you now, that is no excuse to eat. Again, *food is not love.*

One further comment about food and love: some of us use food to love ourselves. That's what we're doing when we reward ourselves with food. If we use food to love ourselves, we are also using the old parental equation of food-equals-love.

● FOOD AND ANGER ●

Conscious or unconscious anger, directed either at yourself or others, is a common motivation for eating. Food intake can and does express anger at other people and at yourself. It also suppresses anger. The unconscious equation goes something like this: I am angry at him. I'd like to do something to that guy. I can't show my anger (for whatever reason; usually because the person, the boss or husband or wife, is in control of the situation). *They* can't control *me*! I'll eat my head off.

This reaction is felt simply as the urge to eat when you recognize that you are angry, or even if you don't. If you get a sudden urge to eat, see if you are angry or annoyed, even slightly. There's a lot more anger in your unconscious.

What do you do with your anger if you can't express it to the person you're angry at? Very often you are much more afraid of the expression of anger than of the actual consequences the expression is likely to bring about. The unconscious fantasy, which you are not aware of, is the fear of loss of control, fear of enormous rage, fear of loss of love from the other person, fear that if you started getting angry you couldn't stop (which is really fear of loss of control). In my experience there are really very few situations in which you cannot say something which might discharge some of the anger. You *can* stop. You *have* got control; you exercise it every day of your life.

Often, once you express the anger, the person to whom you express it has more respect for you. Also, your anger does not necessarily have to be expressed in an angry way. You can say, very coolly, "I am angry at you because . . ." or "I didn't really appreciate what you did . . ."

We are all afraid of the person getting angry in return. Tell me, what's so terrible if somebody gets angry at you? Are you going to fall apart? Will you start to cry? If so, why? Is it uncomfortable? Yes, it's uncomfortable, but can we stand some discomfort? (If we can't stand some discomfort, we can't go on a diet!) Does anger mean the person doesn't love you? Is your relationship to the person so fragile that if they get angry it will be destroyed?

Let's follow an example. The boss hired you because he needs the services you have to offer. If you are dissatisfied, you don't perform those services as well. He knows that. Therefore, if you tell him you're dissatisfied, he may do something about whatever is making you dissatisfied. But, yes, sometimes this is not the case. Sometimes you fear that an expression of anger would get you fired because you are "easily replaceable," and you don't want to take the chance. Then don't, but don't eat, either! That's the old "He can't control me . . . I'll eat my head off" syndrome. Just because you can't express anger doesn't mean you have to eat. In fact, as is obvious, eating only makes you more angry.

● CAN YOU *PAY* TO BE THIN? ●

Tell me, how much would you pay to be thin? Most of my patients say something like "everything I have," or "every penny I own." A pound of chopped meat costs about $1.90, depending on where you live. Would you waste 95 cents—one-half a pound of meat—if I said it would make you thin? But, you say, it's such a shame to waste food. Other people go hungry. Did you ever realize that the food you waste can't possibly be brought to them? I had one patient who said, "But the animal died to give us food. What a shame to waste it." Eating it won't bring the animal back to life.

As I said, how much would you pay to be thin? If I told you to go home and throw out all the junk food you have in the house, all the spaghetti (50 cents a pound), all the cookies, candy, donuts, ice cream, cake . . . well, you know, everything, without eating it up or waiting to go on a diet until you finish all the crap in the house, would you? Could you? What about going out to eat? Can you waste food in a restaurant? You're paying for it, you say (as if we didn't pay for home food). Did you ever notice thin-people in restaurants? They leave one-third of their food, not always, but often. (We can't leave one-third of our food anyplace!)

How much would you pay to be thin? If it's not on your diet, leave it! Be generous with yourself. If your kid comes home with a box of cookies, throw them out! Ruin them before they go into the garbage pail. Put water on them. It's too easy to reach into the garbage pail in a food frenzy. Who said kids have to have junk food? Junk food is used in the most deleterious way, as a reward. There we go again: food as a reward. Give the kid a piece of fruit for a reward if you have to use food as a reward. Don't say "I have to keep it around because my kids eat it." Face it: you eat it.

The unconscious aspect of all of this goes back to being a good little girl or boy and not wasting food, which would incur our family's anger and make us feel, you guessed it, unloved. Wasting food even takes on moral tones sometimes. It's a sin to waste food. You're even losing God's love! It is also a sin, if you want to call it that, to hate yourself. It is a sin to be fat because that's not the way God intended man to look.

The feeling that it's a sin to waste food is with us unconsciously if we were brought up that way, and we may still feel it today. Well, if it's a sin to waste food, then don't buy anything you shouldn't eat and should throw out. The other question that's involved here is, "Why should my family diet if I diet?" The answer is simple: nobody needs junk food. The other members of your family can have plenty of meat, fruit and vegetables in your home, and if they have to have junk food, they can eat it outside the house.

The money you save by not spending it on junk food can easily cover the cost of the small amount of good food a dieter needs to sustain life. The fact of the matter is, no diet is too expensive. Even the all-protein diets, which advocate about eight ounces of protein per day, cost about $2.00 a day. Would you pay $14.00 per week to lose weight? Don't use money or wasting food as an excuse to prevent yourself from losing weight. You *can pay* to lose weight.

CHAPTER 3

SEX
INTIMACY
AND EATING

• UNCONSCIOUS FEARS •

One of the most common unconscious reasons for not losing weight successfully is fear of the opposite sex. Some of you know this fear consciously, but you may not associate it with overeating and being fat. One part of such a fear is fear of closeness, fear of intimacy; another is fear of sex.

Let's take fear of closeness first. Americans have a hangup about closeness, at least outside the family. You're not supposed to tell your intimate secrets to everyone; otherwise, they wouldn't be intimate and secret. That's the definition of closeness, letting someone know your inner thoughts and secrets, your real feelings, the real you. Closeness also means feeling secure that the other person both understands and will not tell anyone else; which means trust is involved, trust that this person will not hurt you, trust that they mean it when they say they understand you or love you, trust that they have your best interests at heart.

Fat-persons are particularly likely to have trouble with some aspects of trust. It is so hard to believe that somebody loves us when we are fat. The problem, of course, is that we don't love ourselves, and we can't see how anybody else could love us. We forget, some of us, that we are people, not just balls of fat. We think fat covers up everything, including what may be an appealing personality. Or, if we think we are loved for our personality, we still don't think anybody could love or accept our fatness, so we still have a hard time believing them. Many of us fear this closeness and literally protect ourselves from it with a wall of fat.

Why do we fear closeness? Because, at the bottom of it all, we are often afraid that closeness will lead to our being "found out," discovered, to be empty, to be nothing, to be worthless, or stupid, or generally unacceptable. We may also be afraid that we will be found out to be someone who really hates the opposite sex or who is full of hate and anger in general.

If this sounds like tough stuff, it is. If it sounds like it doesn't apply to you, that may be true; it may not. But remember: if you do feel this way, you feel it *unconsciously*. You can be sure that something of what I just said is there in your unconscious if you are indeed afraid of the opposite sex, if you are consciously afraid you have nothing to say, for example, in a social situation. You know you have a lot of unconscious hate or anger if, in your dreams, people are always getting killed, either in accidents or by murder. (People dying in dreams can also be evidence of anger, but such deaths can mean other things as well, such as depression. Obviously this depends on the circumstances of the dream.) Sometimes being overly solicitous or overly nice to someone can indicate anger toward them or fear of them.

I am certainly not saying that we hate everybody we love. I am saying that it is more common to hate people we love than it is to hate strangers. The opposite of love is not hate, it is indifference. Think about the people whom you hate, excepting dictators, politicians, etc. Usually, the man or woman you hate is someone who is involved with you in some way, someone you work for or with, someone whom you "have" to care about, like a mother-in-law, or somebody whom you *do* care about or love. When you really don't care about people, you are indifferent to them; what they say or do makes no difference to you.

Once you realize that, excepting political figures, you can only really hate someone with whom you are involved in some way, you need to think of the relationship between your hatred and your eating.

Basically, one good reason for hating someone is that he or she controls or threatens you or your life in some very important way, job, school, money, etc. When someone tries to control us, we have a favorite way of dealing with it: eating. ("You can't control me totally. I still have one area that I can control, and that's my intake of food." Or again, as when mother tried to control us at an age when we had no other area of control: "You can't control me. I'll eat my head off.")

• UNCONSCIOUS FEARS ABOUT THE OPPOSITE SEX •

If you are a fat teenager or have never married, and have been fat since the beginning of puberty, it is fair to say that you may have some problem about the opposite sex. Fat protects us from the social interaction with the opposite sex that we fear and that would be far more likely if we were attractive. (The same is true if you are homosexual, fat, and have never lived with one person longer than, let's say, one year. You may be afraid of your own physical attractiveness, and you may be afraid of closeness.)

Closeness involves sharing the most intimate details of our feelings about ourselves with another. Closeness involves dependency. You depend on the people you are close to to help you get through rough emotional periods and to always be there when you need them. Closeness involves love.

Think of the people, of the same sex or opposite, who you have been close to. You could probably say you loved them. Closeness involves openness. When we open up to someone, we become closer to them. When we express our real feelings to someone else and that person shares his or her feelings with us, we are closer. This closeness involves mutual sharing, especially about how we feel about ourselves.

Most of us fat-people don't think very well of ourselves now, and we didn't in the past. That's why we got fat. Now we are afraid to get close, afraid to depend on another person, because we have an exaggerated fear of losing that person.

In my experience, fat-persons have been rejected far more often than thin-persons, if only for their fat. Fat-persons have, understandably, become wary of getting close and really opening up for fear of alienating the other person and losing him or her.

We fat-persons are often down on ourselves and often depressed. We feel we can't keep telling a person close to us how bad we feel about ourselves; that if we do, the person will reject us, and in some instances we are right.

Let's take a closer look at rejection. For people who fear intimacy and closeness, the usual question to be asked is, "Why do you fear closeness?" The usual answer is, "Because I'll get hurt, because I've gotten hurt so often in the past." Is it just possible that you masterminded or engineered your own rejections, either because you couldn't reject the other person straight out or because you had unconsciously lost interest? No, you say, "I really loved this guy and another woman came along. Worse, he said he loved me, too." Well, sometimes love affairs break up. That doesn't mean that every love affair you will have will break up, unless, by being fat, you are asking men to "jump a hurdle" in their relationships with you.

The chances are that's exactly what you're doing. If you're getting hurt in every relationship, then, I say, you are in control of these situations and *you* are engineering or quarterbacking your own rejection, either before it gets too close or after it has gotten too close for your comfort. You are afraid of closeness, *not* afraid of being hurt. Now, there are dozens of reasons why people fear being close. Many of these come down to being afraid of someone's knowing you, which really means their knowing how low your self-esteem is, or knowing that you are really empty or that, in your opinion, you're really not a good person.

Fear of closeness can also mean fear of domination or control, the inability to trust for any number of reasons. These come down to problems of power, or the inability to see one's own power in a relationship, or the inability to handle the reciprocal power relationships that are a part of any love relationship. If you have serious problems with self-esteem, closeness, trust, power, or dominance, being fat is making them worse, not better (as was the unconscious intention). You will so raise your self-esteem if you lose weight that your whole outlook on relationships will change.

Your outlook will change for the better if you can understand that fatness is falsely protecting you from closeness; that you, not your fat, are protecting you from closeness; that you're using fat, and that, if you want to, you can protect yourself from closeness if you are thin. Once you realize this, you can get thin and see if, and what, changes take place in your relationships.

Closeness between a man and a woman often breeds a natural desire for physical intimacy in fat people, just as it does in thin people. That is where being fat hurts the most—in the bedroom. There, in front of another, you have to show yourself naked. There, you have to face the rolls of fat; you have to face your self-hatred. There, you get that sinking feeling: how could anybody go to bed with this! Not "me" . . . "this!" Of course, there are varying degrees of self-digust, depending on how fat you are, but the bedroom is a painful place for fat-persons. No wonder so many of us shy away from sexual relationships and closeness. Of course, you know how we shy away—by staying fat!

There are also unconscious reasons for fear of closeness and fear of sex. The content of your fantasies and dreams reveals what's in your unconscious, of course, but so does the content of some of your conscious thoughts. For example, if you have many thoughts that are negative about people, if you're hyper-critical, chances are you're also negative and critical about yourself inside. If you find fault with yourself all the time over issues other than your being fat, the chances are that your unconscious image of yourself is terrible and that you are afraid anybody who got close to you would find out all these faults and reject you. So you get fat, make yourself unattractive, "put a wall around you" so people, or a person of the opposite sex, can't get close to you.

• FEAR OF SEX •

The unconscious reason that keeps some people fat or unable to diet successfully is "fear" of sex itself. This applies to all ages, both sexes, homosexual or straight, married or single, sexually active or not—just because someone engages in sex doesn't mean they can't be afraid of it, dislike it, or be afraid of losing control. It may not be exactly fear or be experienced as fear. It may be that you think sex is dirty unconsciously and consciously because you were brought up that way.

Most of us who are over 30 today had parents who were brought up by Victorian parents, to whom sex was something dirty, not to be talked about, shameful or even sinful, except in marriage. Victorian parents rarely showed affection toward each other in front of their children. "Dirty" words and sexual jokes were responded to with varying degrees of anger, disgust, washing the mouth out with soap, or a quick visit to church or the priest. Even thinking sexual thoughts was wrong, sinful, or dirty, and productive of guilt.

If this all seems like history too ancient to have relevance today, consider that up until 1971 or so, the T.V. networks would not show a husband and wife lying in bed together to go to sleep, let alone kissing in bed. So many of our parents, who had Victorian parents, were guilty about their own sexual desires and thoughts — and practices, for that matter. They may not have been as uptight about sex as their parents were, but the guilt, shame, and sin filtered down to us. That is why there are plenty of us today who think we are liberated, yet suffer unconsciously from guilt or disgust over sex.

Think for a moment about your own background, your upbringing. Was one of your parents, especially the parent of the opposite sex, not affectionate toward you? Think about your religious upbringing. What was said about "fornication?" What was said or not said about sex? Think about the sex education you received at the hands of your parents, even if it was someone other than a parent who informed you of the "facts of life." If your parents didn't, or couldn't, talk to you about sex, the automatic implication was that there was something forbidden or dirty about sex. For women: Did your mother talk to you about menstruation before you got your first period? For men: Did your father or mother tell you about getting girls pregnant before you were twelve or so?

Did your parents kiss each other in front of you, or hold each other? Did your parents refuse to let you go out on dates until you were 16 or 17? I had a patient whose father told her, when she was 12, not to let a boy maul her. Remembering this warning, she became terribly distraught at 15 when she was petting with her boyfriend and enjoyed it. Her father's use of the word "maul" implied that petting was not only wrong and dirty but was, as well, a violation of herself. This is another concept that many of us have in our unconscious minds, that sex is a violation of our bodies, of our privacy, and, often, a violation of our rights.

This concept is more common among women than it is among men. Things have changed since Victorian times, but men in our society are still allowed more sexual freedom than women and are less likely to feel guilty about their sexual desires and practices. Even if a man does feel guilty about sex,

51

he's still likely to enjoy sex more than a woman feeling the same amount of guilt. It is easier for him to override the guilt because enjoyment itself is not as charged with guilt for a man as it is for a woman. You see, you may not particularly feel that unconsciously guilty about sex per se, yet may feel guilty about enjoying it, just as you feel guilty about enjoying food. Our whole society has hangups about enjoyment and pleasure, especially intense pleasure, especially sexual pleasure. How many of us were taught, "everything in moderation"!

There seems to be a prohibition in our society against extremes that often applies to sex and to being fat. "Don't overdo it." "Easy does it." This prohibition against extremes prevents a lot of people from letting go in bed, letting themselves get excited, letting themselves have an orgasm, even letting themselves try different positions or oral-genital sex. I am not recommending that you go to extremes in everything, just in sex. What's wrong with that?

Many women will say, "I just can't let go." I would question, first, the relationship that you have with your partner, and second, whether he knows how to stimulate you effectively. If you have been able to have an orgasm while masturbating, as most women can, but not while making love, then the chances are that your partner doesn't know how best to stimulate you and that you need to be open enough to be able to tell him what turns you on. According to the Hite report, for example, 25 percent of women need manual stimulation of the clitoris as well as vaginal penetration in order to achieve orgasm. But, you say, he does that and I still don't come. Either you need to let go, lose a little control, or you need to think about your feelings for your partner. Are you angry with him? Do you resent him? Do you "submit" to sex when you're not in the mood? Do you feel controlled by him both in your relationship with him and in bed? Do you love him?

For the majority of people, male or female, there's no aphrodisiac that can beat love. Yet love is not a prerequisite for a good sexual experience. The reverse may, in fact, be true. Many people have the problem that they can't think of love and sex as being together. When they love someone they don't feel strongly sexual, and if they have sex without love, they denigrate their partner. This takes another form with fat-persons of either sex. It goes like this: If he or she wants to have sex with me, he must love me because no one would want this body otherwise; but, if he wants to have sex with me, he wants me for sex, because no one could love me in this body. But how could he want me for sex?

In this situation, the fat-person ends up feeling used for sex and unlovable besides. The feelings are almost all unconscious — only occasionally are they consciously felt and identified. The fat-person feels only a reticence to go to bed.

• FAT, FREUD, AND FOOD •

Other unconscious reasons for "fear" of sex can be seen in the workings of the Oedipus complex. Small children may or may not actually say that when they grow up they'd like to marry Daddy or Mommy, but nearly all of them particularly want love and attention from the parent of the opposite sex. Most of us, in fact, learn to love the opposite sex by first learning to love the parent of the opposite sex.

We especially want love and attention when we are teenagers, which is why we so vehemently insist that our parent of the opposite sex leave us alone, and why we have so many fights with the parent of the same sex. We are really fighting for the love of the opposite-sex parent. We also fight often with the parent of the opposite sex since this is a way of avoiding the sexual attraction that exists on both sides.

This sexual attraction between parents and children during the teenage years is normal and natural and usually unconscious. All that there is to indicate the unconscious attraction is the conscious anger, repulsion, fighting, hatred, and sometimes love that exists between the child and the parents of both sexes, for the reasons just given. Now, what does this all have to do with fear of sex? Let's go a little further.

Very often, in looking for a mate, we unconsciously look for certain qualities that characterized our parent of the opposite sex. We may well feel that our mate is outwardly and inwardly totally different from our opposite-sex parent. Sometimes, however, he or she really does have emotional qualities that are similar to those of our opposite-sex parent. If you never gave up your parent, in an emotional sense, if you never gave up your need for and attachment to your parent, and if you married someone who resembles your parent emotionally, then you may find it difficult to enjoy sex with your partner. You may unconsciously feel that sex with him or her is dirty or disgusting, a feeling you get because, in an unconscious sense, you are sleeping with your parent.

For those of you who don't enjoy sex with your more-or-less permanent partner and do enjoy it with other men or women, I suggest you think closely about what I have just said. The same goes for those of you who feel dirty or disgusted about sex.

Now, what does all this have to do with being fat? Fat makes us unattractive, we assume or even hope, which means that we hope no one will want to have sex with us, which means that the unconscious feelings of guilt and disgust won't be stimulated.

● FAT AND FANTASIES ●

There are other sexual reasons for staying fat and unattractive. Many people have a fantasy, be it conscious or unconscious, that if they were thin and attractive to the opposite sex, they would go wild sexually. They would have intercourse with everybody in sight, or have an affair. This fantasy is more common among women than men, because men are "allowed" to have intercourse with everybody in sight. Yet the truth underlying the fantasy applies equally to both sexes: it is our own sexual urges that we fear, not the advances of the opposite sex.

Married men do have fear fantasies about having an affair, but theirs go one step further. They are afraid they will find a woman ten or twenty years younger and break up their family to marry the younger woman, which a number of men in their forties seem to be doing these days. Women seem to be less worried about breaking up the family and more worried about an affair. Remember, these concerns may be unconscious. What you experience is the effect of them, the inability to lose weight and keep it off.

Suppose you have consciously thought of having an affair, whether you're male or female, and then you have also thought that you probably couldn't get the partner you want because you are fat. You may even feel that if you were attractive you would be drawn into an affair, whether you really wanted one or not; that you couldn't handle being attractive, which means you couldn't handle sexual advances, either because you can't say no, or because you really want to go to bed with several people. Then there is the guilt over all of these thoughts, guilt for wanting an affair, either consciously or unconsciously.

Some people feel that even thinking about an affair is being unfaithful to their mate. Yet most people, of course, have entertained the idea of having intercourse with someone other than their mate at one time or another, even if it is for a brief moment, even if it only goes as far as seeing someone and thinking he or she is attractive (your unconscious goes much further). But what if you know you would have an affair if you got thinner, yet are afraid of the consequences, including the guilt?

I think we all have a lot more control over ourselves than we give ourselves credit for. If you know you would have an affair if you were thinner, then you want one now, so admit it to yourself. What's wrong with wanting one? We want a lot of things in this world that we can't have, such as food when we're on a diet. You say, "But it's wrong to want one." If you feel guilty for wanting an affair, then go ahead and feel guilty. The guilt will probably prevent you from having one, if you want to use that as your control. Fine, but don't prevent yourself from having an affair by eating.

Actions do indeed speak louder than thoughts or words; and you have control over your actions, if not over your desires and fantasies. Waiting in line for a movie is a typical example. We all want to go to the front of the line, but we don't. We control ourselves. We control our desire to spend money we don't have, because we don't like the consequences of being in debt. We can control ourselves, when we want to have an affair, if we don't want the consequences of being found out or the guilt we would feel.

Suppose the desire for an affair is totally unconscious. How do you know it's there, and what do you do about it? Examine your dreams and fantasies. If you dream about strange men or have sexual fantasies about strange men, or about men you know, then you may want an affair (there are other reasons for dreaming or fantasizing about strange men). Fantasize: Let yourself go about what would happen if you were thin. What is the first thing that comes into your mind about the opposite sex when you picture yourself as thin? Usually the first thought is that you'd be attractive to men (or women). What does *that* mean? If the fantasy stops there, fine. Does it? See for yourself. If your first thought was that your mate would find you more attractive, you may be fat for other reasons, which we will take up shortly.

If you identify with the idea that you are fat because you are afraid that you will have an affair or go wild sexually, then you are ready to recognize that you do have the control to stop yourself from doing these things if doing them is not what you really want.

Further, you are ready to analyze why you would want to have an affair or go wild. Is it because you are unhappy with your marriage? Why? Is it because you have a reasonably good marriage, but a poor sex life? If so, why do you have a poor sex life? Is the problem you, your husband, or both of you? Does he ejaculate too rapidly? Can you have an orgasm with him? These kinds of problems can be cured or helped if you seek professional aid. Certainly food won't help you in such a situation.

Does your husband respond poorly to your obesity? Do you respond poorly to his sexual stimulation because of your obesity or embarrassment? Not only does food not help you in this situation, but it makes matters worse. Whatever the problems in your relationship or your sex life, if you and your husband face them together, you have a chance of solving them. Facing them together can mitigate your fears of going wild or having an affair.

Suppose you want an affair for variety, but are staying fat to avoid the opportunity. Being thin offers you choices; it offers you freedom. The key issue is that you do have control, when you're thin, not to have the affair, if that's what you want. You are free to be attractive to your husband if the marriage is good and you want to be faithful, you have the freedom of attracting someone new, if that's what you want.

You don't have to stay fat to keep yourself in prison or under control. Chances are, unless you weigh 250 pounds (and sometimes even then) you could have an affair right now if you sought it. The fat isn't really stopping you anyway. You are stopping you, using fat as an excuse. "Who would have me the way I look now?" If you don't want to find out the answer to that question, then don't ask it.

Understanding the reasons why you would want an affair may help you get over the guilt of wanting it, which may help you stop eating and building your own prison. It may clarify for you that you have every reason to want an affair. If your marriage isn't going well, for whatever reasons, and you have never thought of having an affair or being married to someone else, think again. It is the most natural thing in the world to fantasize about another person or another marriage if you are unhappy in your own. If you are not doing this, you are probably suppressing these thoughts from consciousness. They are alive and thriving in your unconscious, however, where they can effectively keep you from losing weight.

• BECAUSE OF FAT •

But what if you feel that your marriage and sex life are bad because you're fat; that your mate can't stand your fat; that fat is what's ruining your sex life and the relationship? If this were true, and the marriage were healthy otherwise, I would suggest that you have other unconscious reasons for not losing weight. Otherwise you, as the fat person, would have all the motivation in the world for losing weight. It's more often the case, however, that couples use the fat as an excuse or explanation as to why things are not going well between them.

It is, of course, true that obesity does make us unattractive. Many men and women object to the fatness, and this objection is often expressed as a decrease in the frequency of sexual contact. Fatness itself is especially likely to be interfering with the relationship in cases where the woman has gotten fat with pregnancy and never lost the weight.

• PREGNANCY FAT •

First, let me say that anybody who has gotten fat with pregnancy and has not taken the weight off for two years after the last pregnancy is keeping it on for some reason other than that it is hard to lose weight or that she's too busy with the kids. The busier you are, the easier it is to lose weight. "It's too hectic with two or three small children. I can't concentrate on losing weight," you say. There *is* something to that. Are you stuck in the house and always around food? Well, I can't accept that. The probable reason you eat is because you resent being stuck in the house, especially if you worked before the children came along. Being fat is an unconscious way of being unattractive, so you won't be subject to sex relations as often, so you won't get pregnant again, so you won't be stuck in the house.

Suppose you got fat during or after pregnancy for the first time and haven't lost the weight. What can you do? First, try to identify your unconscious reasoning. "The child will hold us together. My life is set. I don't have to be attractive anymore." Or, "I resent staying in the house all day. I have no outside stimulation. I'm bored." Or, "I resent the child who keeps me tied down and not working." Or even, "I resent my husband for his freedom, for his working and for his giving me this child."

Now, suppose one or more of these unconscious attitudes are really there. What can you do about them? First, if you identify with any of these reasons, you have, by doing so, succeeded in making them conscious. Face your resentment of your situation, your resentment of your husband and child. It's okay. Since you are creating, to a certain extent, the situation that you resent, there is no need for guilt over this resentment. Face the fact that it is you who are responsible for your sitting home with a two-year-old child and not doing at least one thing per week for outside stimulation. If you can afford this book, you can afford a baby-sitter once a week so that you can do something different. Food won't help you now.

Don't fall into the trap of thinking, "If he loved me thin, he should love me fat," as if fat were outside ourselves and didn't count because we are still ourselves underneath the fat. Fat *is* a part of our selves. It can't be discounted by those around us, even those who love us; which gets us back to the old "He should love me for myself," as if fat were not a part of our self.

"I exist independently of my fat," you say. Yes, and that is what enables you to lose weight. That is what enables some men to say "I love you, but I don't like the fact that you are fat." Yet when fatness interferes with a relationship, it isn't so easy to separate the person who is fat from the fact that they are fat. It isn't easy, because people who are fat feel bad about themselves and don't love themselves. Unable to relate as well to their spouses because they don't love themselves, they need more love, want more affection and reassurance *because* they are fat.

In such a situation, at the very moment that there is need for reassurance on the part of the fat person, there is sometimes a backing off on the part of the spouse, all of this taking place unconsciously on both people's parts. What comes out is the fighting, often over the children and household chores, the decreased frequency of lovemaking ("We're too tired, with three kids and all," the husband's working hard and late because he doesn't want to come home because the "romance" has gone out of his marriage, leading his wife to suspect he's playing around, leading to more fights; and on and on.

Obviously, not all of these problems are necessarily due to fat. Just as obviously, however, fatness makes them worse. Fatness makes almost everything worse. Fighting over the household chores, for instance, usually occurs because the husband thinks his work stops at five o'clock and he need not work at home by getting the children to bed or cleaning up the kitchen after dinner. The woman feels she has too much work to do, the man feels "That's all she has to do all day," and adds (if he's angry) ". . . the fat slob."

Many men feel this way about the woman's role anyway, and a husband who comes home late may simply be a compulsive worker or may really have that much work to do. Still, if his wife is fat, her excess weight can aggravate the situation because, unconsciously, he is less sexually attracted to her no matter how much he loves her.

What about the unconscious attitude that "I've got him (or her) now and I don't have to worry about being attractive"? With today's divorce rate of 50 percent or more, I don't think anyone can afford to think that way. You say, "But if he or she really loves me, it wouldn't or shouldn't matter if I get fat. I should be loved through thick and thin" — literally.

Well, if obesity didn't cause so many secondary problems, that might be the case, in a very strong love relationship; but the secondary problems are enormous. There is a decrease in sexual attraction on the part of the spouse. There is the inevitable involvement with the spouse over issues of diet and dieting. There is the decrease of self-esteem on the part of the fat-person, resulting in hypersensitivity around all issues of criticism, whether or not the criticism comes down to weight. The decreased self-esteem spills over into the bedroom, with attendant consciousness of fatness and placement of fat rolls in bed, which leads to an attendant decrease in sexual responsiveness because of the spectator role that we take. (We are watching ourselves, the way we look and perform.)

What do you do about this? Start by facing the fact that fat is part of you, that you may be loved in spite of it, but that you are foisting something undesirable on your mate. If your obesity leads to sexual problems, directly or indirectly, you can't sit back and say "I've got him" (or her) with any certainty whatsoever.

CHAPTER 4

LOVE
ME
TENDER

Suppose, you say, your husband or wife loves you fat or thin. There is nothing wrong with your sex life. Your marriage is going very well and you don't identify with any of the unconscious motivations I have mentioned so far. You're not afraid you might have an affair or be promiscuous if you were thin, but you are fat and you want to lose weight. What then? Well, let's examine some of the more subtle, not-so-obvious reasons for not losing weight.

Women in our society are taught to be "feminine." If you think of some synonyms for "feminine," what comes to mind are words like: soft, soft-spoken, gentle, passive, graceful, slender, wispy, petite, quiet, submissive, tender, and dainty. Dainty, petite, slender, wispy, and graceful are impossible things to be when you're fat. In fact, it is damned hard to feel "feminine" when you're fat.

It is also, physically, damned hard to be "pushed around" when you're fat, and some fat women translate that into an emotional feeling and feel less controllable, less "pushable aroundable," when they are fat. Further, many highly intellectual fat women unconsciously feel that they would be taken as a sex object, or not be taken as seriously, or not be given as much credence if they were thin. This has some validity in today's world, since men still first relate to women, even in business, as sex objects. Fatness, bigness, conveys a certain sense of power to a person. Power and femininity do not "go" in most people's minds. So some women unconsciously equate power, personal power, with fatness. Your being passive and submissive means that somebody else is being active, aggressive, and dominant. If you equate thinness with femininity, and femininity with submissiveness, and submissiveness with being controlled or dominated, it's no wonder you're still fat.

I had this particular unconscious problem, and what I realized was that my own unconscious was a male chauvinist. Indeed, unconsciously I looked at women as vulnerable and powerless and feared thinness because, to me, thinness meant being taken as a sex object. Well, you know, when I lost all the weight, people respected me more! I was complimented on my control and I had more personal power, especially as a doctor, than ever before.

If you equate femininity with vulnerability, etc., then your unconscious is probably a male chauvinist (of course, you can be a woman and still be a male chauvinist), and you probably fear being thin because you would look upon yourself as vulnerable and powerless. Well, all I can tell you is, get thin—you won't lose an ounce of personal power. You will be respected by important people more, and, most important, you will respect yourself.

Men also feel that they have a sense of personal power if they are . . . big, shall we say. They have the same feeling that they are listened to more, that their opinion holds more weight (pun intended), that figuratively, and sometimes literally, they can't be pushed around, and that, strangely, they have more "animal magnetism" for women.

• STRANGE UNCONSCIOUS REASONING •

A woman may be fat "because" she has a fat mother, or "because" she has a thin mother. If this seems paradoxical, think about the psychodynamics involved. If she has a thin mother, unconsciously she may not want to compete, or she may be afraid of actually winning the competition between her and her mother for the father's love and attention. She may associate thinness with vulnerability, depending on the way her father treated her mother, and hence make the unconscious equation fat=power.

If she has a fat mother, she unconsciously believes that she will definitely win the competition if she gets thin, and so she gets or stays fat. Also, the process of identification can work toward a daughter's being fat with a fat mother. If the fat mother is dominant in the family, or if fatness is associated with motherhood or *motherness*, as it is in some ethnic groups in the United States, the unconscious wish is to be like Mommy because "that's what a woman is." This process of identification is normal and accounts for the fact that most children, especially daughters, grow up thin if their mothers are thin. You might say that fat-persons with thin mothers have a "failure" of identification, for a variety of reasons we'll discuss in this chapter ("I don't want to be like her. She is too vulnerable, too helpless"—too whatever.) Other failures of identification are boys' becoming delinquent (when they have "good, productive" fathers); or boys and girls getting into drugs when they have "good, church-going" parents.

If we can grow up fat with either a thin mother or a fat mother, how come everybody doesn't grow up fat? First, not everybody deals with Oedipal emotions by eating. Second, the child, at four or five, figures unconsciously that the best way to win the love of the parent of the opposite sex is to be like the parent of the same sex, who won that love in the first place. This, in fact, is how we all end up with "female" or "male" emotional and behavioral attributes. We first imitate the parent of the same sex. By identifying with the parent of the same sex, we solve the Oedipal problems. If, for any reason, they cannot identify with the parent of the same sex, fat-persons take it out by getting fat.

Why do fat-persons take everything out in being fat? This is actually the definition of a fat-person, somebody who learned, perhaps in infancy, perhaps later, that food assuages all emotions and that fat offers various forms of literal or emotional protection from unconscious wishes and external threats.

A man may stay fat because, unconsciously, he doesn't want to be like his thin father, who may have hurt him, or whom he may not have respected. This is also quite true for women and their mothers. It is particularly true for teenage girls who have seen their mothers play the "helpless female" role and who reject that role or some other role. It is true for men whose mothers were dominant and who understood unconsciously that their fathers were being dominated or controlled, as it is for teenage girls who see their mothers dominated or controlled.

What is being rejected here is a concept of the parent of the same sex which includes their thinness. The unconscious equation is fat=power; the unconscious mechanism, "I take in what I want. You can't control me." The child is rejecting the role that the parents play.

I am not saying that little boys unconsciously want to be girls, though there are a few feelings like that buried in every man's unconscious. On the other hand, not a few women unconsciously want to be men, and many even hold this idea consciously if they think about it. It is not too difficult to understand why more women want to be men than men want to be women. Men have had all the power, both in the home and outside it, for eons of time. More women than men are fat, too!

Some men fear that they will look less masculine or more feminine if they are thin. (Women don't ordinarily worry about looking more masculine if they lose weight. It is more common for a woman to fear looking more feminine, for some of the reasons just given.) Men, particularly short men, fear looking feminine because they are afraid of loss of personal power; but some men also unconsciously fear that they will look like a homosexual, or that they will be more subject to approaches by homosexuals. There are also men who are afraid of their own unconscious homosexuality; who stay fat because it protects them from feeling feminine, or from being subject to the approaches of homosexuals, or from getting in touch with their own homosexual desires.

There is one almost sure way to determine whether or not you have unconscious homosexual fears or desires. Ask yourself how you feel about homosexuals, and give some thought to the intensity of those feelings. If you hate homosexuals vehemently, if they disgust you, if you think they should all be put in jail, the chances are that you are "protesting too much," that you may be disgusted with them because, unconsciously, you are attracted to them.

What about women and homosexuality? Women in our society are allowed to touch, hug, dance together, kiss, hold hands on the street, along with other, more subtle expressions of affection, expressions that some would describe as homosexual contact. Love between women can be more openly stated than love between men. A woman has no qualms about saying she loves her next-door female neighbor, but a man is unlikely to come out and say he loves your neighbor's husband. Since a woman can love another woman without being called homosexual, women are less threatened by feelings for their own sex than are men. They are even less threatened by thoughts of actual homosexuality. An exception is teenage girls and women who have never married. Those two groups worry a little more; and again, they worry unconsciously, rarely consciously.

Does this mean that if you have unconscious homosexual urges you are a homosexual? Not at all. In fact, all of us, male or female, have a few homosexual urges in our unconscious.

Obviously, these are overridden by the usually greater heterosexual urge. Most people have thought of what it would be like to make love to a member of the same sex and most people are slightly repulsed by the idea, which is normal. But these people don't make a big issue out of being repulsed by homosexuality; they don't go around calling people queer or faggots at every turn. Teenage boys do, and they are in fact "defending" against their own homosexual urges which have sprung up with the awakening of the sex drive in general.

The point is not that homosexuality is normal or abnormal, but that occasional homosexual thoughts are normal. Some men, in particular, won't get thin because, unconsciously, they fear that they would look effeminate and would be subject to homosexual advances; others fear seduction by a homosexual because of their own unconscious homosexual urges.

If, after reading this, you feel that homosexual fears in your unconscious may be keeping you from losing weight, how do you get rid of them? First of all, if you can identify with what I've said, you have already made your unconscious fears conscious. Second, you need to decide whether you have fears or wishes. Sometimes it's the wishes that cause homosexual fears. You can reassure yourself that you have control over your actions, that even in the fact of an unconscious wish you needn't run around being afraid of your unconscious.

Most important, if you have identified with any of the unconscious entities I have mentioned, then you have already gone a long way. You have made your unconscious conscious, which is the first step in dealing with it, and you have made the important connection between your overweight and your unconscious fears. Once that connection is made, the unconscious fear or wish loses a great deal of its power to keep you fat.

• FAT IN SPADES •

Did you ever see a man who was 70 pounds overweight or more at 50? Did you ever think that he was asking for a heart attack? (Women also, particularly after menopause, have an increased chance for a heart attack if they are obese.) I met a perfect stranger the other day, introduced myself, and told him I was doing a book about being fat. He was fat, and I had the nerve to ask him why, unconsciously, he thought he was fat. After some thought he said, "Self-destruction. Isn't everybody self-destructive?"

Are we all self-destructive, destroying our bodies, our physical and mental health by being fat? Maybe even destroying relationships because we're fat? Did you ever think of suicide because you were fat, lonely, depressed, and feeling unlovable? Did you ever hear the expression "eat yourself into the ground," or "digging your grave with your fork?"

• SHY AND DRY •

It is certainly possible that you have not identified with any of these more common unconscious fears that prevent people from losing weight. But there is one that you may feel does have validity for you: the unconscious, or sometimes conscious, fear of social situations, not because you are fat, but because you are shy, or because you are uncomfortable in social situations. If your fear is conscious, you may have assumed that it is your fat that makes you shy and afraid of being rejected. Actually, it is the other way around. You are fat because you are shy and afraid of being rejected. That's what the fat is there for. It protects you from being rejected for your personality.

The biggest problem of this kind is found among teenagers, whose biggest problem is often knowing what to say, but this problem can extend well beyond the teenage years, particularly in people who have always been shy and fat and have never married. The fear of being rejected for seeming empty or stupid is ever-present. The fat protects you from being approached, so you won't be found out, besides which, if you unconsciously don't think you're a nice person, you can always tell yourself you've been rejected because you're fat and avoid dealing with your unconscious opinion of yourself.

Shyness gives the power of a new relationship to someone else. They speak first. You do what they want to do, you talk about what they want to talk about. Of course, that's the appeal of shyness. You don't have to think of what to say, you don't have to make decisions; you can be "taken care of."

How do you change this pattern? You need to change it in order to lose weight. In conversation, let the conversation happen. Don't try to control it. Don't feel that it's your responsibility to fill in the gaps in a group conversation or that it's your responsibility to keep the conversation going. If it's a one to one conversation, you do have more responsibility. Let the other person draw *you* out. We fat-persons have an ambivalent feeling about control. On the one hand we want to control a lot of things, especially relationships; on the other hand, we want to be passive, to be taken care of, to be swept off our feet, to be dominated sometimes, and to have other people control us, especially our eating.

You have to decide whether you want to be under other people's control or whether you want to be under your own control. You also have to get interested in another person and what he or she has to say and get your mind off yourself and your fears of rejection.

• DEPENDENCY FAT •

The reason many people, fat or not, want to "control" their relationships is to prevent themselves from being hurt. In a way, we don't want to need anybody or anything. If we don't need a person, then we won't be so hurt if he or she leaves us, or says something painful to us. But we all do need the people who are important to us. If we don't, they're not very important.

To the extent that we need people, we have a certain dependency on them, and in our society there is something almost immoral about dependency: "If you want something done, do it yourself"; "You can't depend on anybody but yourself"; "I did it myself." Consider America's watchwords: independence, private enterprise, individual achievement. We are not supposed to depend on anybody. Yet all relationships of any meaning involve dependency, and when you think about it for a minute you can see that dependency is not all bad. If you can depend on someone to always be there when you need them, for instance, that's good.

Do you feel you're not supposed to need them all the time? Is that why you eat? It goes back to the food-is-love concept. We are dependent on the people who are important to us for love, support, problem-solving, money sometimes, companionship, intellectual stimulation, being taken care of, mothering or fathering our children, sexual stimulation, doing things for us that we can't physically or mentally do for ourselves. We often depend on another person for his or her physical presence. We need to know that the other person is there or that there's somebody in the house, even though no interaction may be taking place at the moment.

Compulsive eating can mean that not enough of your dependency needs are being met. Eating is an attempt both to satisfy dependency needs and be independent at the same time. Eating is taking in love *and* taking care of yourself. It is saying "I can take care of myself. I don't need anyone. I don't want anyone to get close to me." Of course we all need love, and love involves dependency. Sometimes, however, when we are too dependent, when we need the love too much, say, from our parents when we're twenty-four, or from our spouse, particularly if we feel very needy or are trying to get the lost love of our parents from our spouse, then we eat.

Am I saying that we shouldn't need the love of our parents when we're twenty-four? Yes and no. It is nice to have the love of our parents when we're grown up, but we ordinarily shift from needing parental love to needing heterosexual love at a particular time in our lives. This shift generally occurs between the ages of eighteen and twenty-five; though we don't want to lose the love of our parents, if we ever had it, we do need heterosexual love more and find it more important to have.

When a parent, particularly an opposite-sex parent, remains all-important, or when a person can't relate to the opposite sex because he or she is too attached to the opposite-sex parent, we have names for the person—Mama's boy or Daddy's girl. Sometimes Mama's boys or Daddy's girls try to get their mate to behave in a maternal or paternal way, or relate to them as if they were their parent, or unconsciously expect them to be like the opposite-sex parent. When the mate can't live up to this emotional behavior, the person may express a continuing need for the parent through eating. The original equation, food is love, established in infancy and early childhood, still holds for many of us fat-persons.

• ADOLESCENT FAT •

Other problems which can prevent some fat-persons from losing weight involve the parent of the same sex. As we grow up, we unconsciously and consciously emulate the behavior of the same-sex parent, including his or her eating behavior, but fat is not just a matter of having bad eating habits because that parent had bad eating habits. There is another, more subtle reason; identification.

74

I have one patient who weighed 260 pounds, whose mother weighed 250 and whose eleven-year-old sister was rapidly becoming fat. It was very clear that the women of this family were afraid to compete with each other for the only male in the family. Therefore, I could not help my patient to lose weight until her mother agreed to lose weight also. As it turned out, this plan did not work; the mother quickly dropped out of the weight competition, leaving the daughter, who was too close to her to begin with, to lose weight on her own. Many parents suddenly turn away from their opposite-sex child at puberty for this very reason. The parent, who is unconsciously attracted to the child, either becomes hypercritical as a defense against the sexual attraction, or in some way alienates the child as a way of cooling off the feelings.

But, you say, teenagers and parents argue about real issues, especially control. The parents want control of the teenager; they want control of his or her hours, when the child does his homework, what he eats (whether he's fat or thin), where he goes, how late he stays out and who he hangs around with. These issues could all be settled very amicably if the child thought of the parents the way adults so often think of a boss — he holds the money, he has the control, I must do as he says, even though I don't like it. The teenager, of course, rebels and accepts the control with poor grace indeed, if at all.

It is psychologically necessary that we rebel in order to detach ourselves from our parents; it's necessary that we establish an identity separate from our parents': our own type of friends, our own cycle of sleep and wakefulness, our own capacity to hold liquor, and so on. If we did not rebel, we would not develop our own minds, our own opinions. We would not be able to make choices because our parents have always made our choices for us. We would not be able to think for ourselves.

Rebellion also has to do with fatness, as do our counter-Oedipal unconscious feelings that make us fat so that we can mitigate the attraction between our opposite-sex parent and ourselves. Rebellion is, again, the "you can't control me I'll eat my head off" syndrome. Rebellion is independence — "I'll eat and drink anything I want when and where I want." Excesses are frequent in adolescence. An excess of food to make up for the love of temporarily forsaken parents may cause a person who is genetically prone to gain weight easily (a fat-person) to become fat as a teenager.

Many fat-persons who have been overprotected, whose healthy adolescent rebellion was successfully put down, find it hard to make decisions and choices. They don't know what they like or dislike. They don't know what they want to do in life or with their time. This is especially true of women when their kids become more independent and they have time on their hands.

These women, having been overprotected by their parents, expect to be overprotected by their husbands. They want someone to make their decisions for them. They want someone who is big and strong to take care of them, tell them what to do, make the "big" choices in life for them. Southern women in particular have, at least by reputation, confused being overprotected with being feminine, and maybe all of us have confused inability to make decisions or being a little silly and frivolous and helpless with being feminine.

If you can lift 40 pounds (a suitcase, say, or a child), and do so on occasion, are you, at that moment, less feminine in your own eyes than a thin woman who would stand there and say, "Oh, I couldn't possibly lift that"? Is it less feminine in your own eyes to say, "I want to go to that movie," than to say, "Oh, I can't decide. You make the choice"?

Do you, consciously or unconsciously, feel that it's more feminine to "give in" all the time, to not take a stand, to depend totally on your husband's mind and abilities? This places a terrible burden on the man, who, in most cases, would like you to help him make big decisions. Are you staying fat to be overprotected and taken care of? Are you staying fat to avoid being feminine, helpless, unable to make decisions?

What if you are married to the kind of man who needs to make all the decisions and control the family in order to feel like a man? If your father was like that too, and you are fat, you may be rebelling or you may be trying to become more "powerful" than you actually feel inside so he can't push you around so much; but if you like being controlled, dependent, having your decisions made for you, why are you fat? (In truth, it may be from another unconscious reason, whether listed here or not, or it may be from unconscious rebellion.)

Men, too, are subject to the problems that arise from their never having rebelled, or their having been overprotected, usually by their mothers. They marry women who take charge. Even if the woman doesn't want to take charge, the man puts her in that position. Some men say that their wives want it this way, and that may be true, but the men want it this way too; and if both they and their wives are fat, neither really wants it that way. What is really going on is a power struggle between them. (Can't they both be happy and content and successful and love each other and not care if they're fat? Yes, *but* . . . If they don't care if they're fat, why is one of them reading this book?

Remember, in some people's unconscious minds, fat is power. Power is control, and some fat couples give service to the old "You can't control me" idea by eating. When both halves of a couple are fat, quite often they either both want control, in which case each seeks to control the other, or neither wants control, in which case each is looking for control from the other.

• PREGNANT MEN •

Occasionally you find a man who got fat during his wife's pregnancy, while she was getting fat in both pregnancy and overeating. Men *do* have unconscious needs or desires to share in the miracle of pregnancy, and these needs come out in various ways. Some men get "morning sickness" early in their wives' pregnancies or get pains in their abdomen or back when the baby is near term. The weight a man may gain while his wife is pregnant is "sympathy fat," like sympathy morning sickness and sympathy abdominal pains.

All this is perfectly normal, but when the pregnancy is over, it is plain hard for both people to lose the weight. The baby makes tremendous demands on the time of both parents and on their energy and sleep. The baby takes attention away from each parent, particularly the man. As his wife's energy and time are taken up by the baby, less attention is given to him. Food is love: he eats. There are some women who give love and attention to the baby almost (or even totally) to the exclusion of their husbands. In such cases, it's no wonder the husband is fat.

• SOME WORDS FOR THE FAT DIVORCÉE •

You may have been fat all your life, or fat since pregnancy, or fat since forty, for whatever reasons. All of a sudden, for whatever reasons, you find yourself divorced and fat. There is a tremendous urgency to lose weight to get back on the mate or relationship market. Yet, there is a tremendous reluctance to enter the mate market and a resentment against having to lose weight, which really is resentment felt toward the party that left and broke up the marriage, or caused the marriage to be so unsatisfactory that you broke it up.

The resentment is understandable. Now the dating games start all over again. Now you have to enter the meat market, and now you have to lose weight. The resentment comes out on having to lose weight when it really belongs to the person who, as you see it, forced you into this position in the first place. Don't resent losing weight. You always wanted to do it in the first place, and secretly you may think that if you had been thin, he or she wouldn't have left. So you really resent yourself, not the fact that you have to lose weight.

The position of having to look for a new mate calls up, unconsciously, all the fears, depressions, elations (if there were any) of adolescence. It calls up all the unconscious feelings attached to the parent of the opposite sex and all of the unconscious reasons for being fat, if these involved the parent of the opposite sex; all the power struggles with parents; all the battles over who has control.

After all, the dating game is often a power struggle of emotions. Who cares for whom? Does she know I like her (as if knowing that you are liked by a person puts them in a weaker position)! It's a power struggle over vulnerability. Who's more vulnerable than whom ("she's alone; she's a divorcée . . . probably hasn't had sex in months. She probably wants it more than I do.") This is the battle of the sexes, and you know what fat-persons do with any battle, any power struggle. They figure that they'll lose, so they make up for the lost self-esteem with — you guessed it — food!

Food is love; food helps you swallow feelings; food is soothing; food alleviates anxiety; food is a social occasion (perhaps an opportunity for prospecting); food is sex; food is "I control myself"; food is the power to reject or accept . . . "No thanks, I don't want any." Food is self-love, and feeding somebody is giving them love.

Divorcées very often are depressed, even though they may be relieved to have had the divorce or to have it over with. They may feel free, but scared. "Scared" is the right word. Fat-persons eat when they are scared, and every divorced person is scared, whether he or she knows it or not: scared about the future, about money, kids, job, sexual responsiveness, adjusting to a different sexual partner; about where and how to meet, and attract, the prospective mate. Loneliness is the big one here, and food is company.

At this point you may have identified with one or more of the unconscious reasons for staying fat that are mentioned in this book, or you may be trying to arrive at reasons of your own that aren't mentioned here. In either case, the following steps may be of help to you in making those unconscious determinants conscious, and thereby robbing them of their power to keep you fat.

• HOW TO GET AT YOUR UNCONSCIOUS •

1. Examine your dreams and your fantasies, particularly flash-fantasies like meeting a handsome man, and, for a split second, making love to him. Your unconscious may make you feel so guilty about this perfectly normal fantasy that you eat.

2. Examine your own history. Were you a Mama's boy or Daddy's girl? If you don't think of yourself as either, who were you close to? This may help you discover whether your problem was one of identification with the loved parent, rebellion, or an attempt to play down your sex appeal because the parent of the opposite sex gave you more attention than the same-sex parent—or whatever. Only you know your own history and your own feelings.

Was either parent fat? If so, what was your relationship to that parent? When did you get fat? The answer to this question tells you the psychodynamics of the period in which you got fat. Did you get fat with pregnancy? Did the baby cement your relationship with your husband so firmly that unconsciously you felt you didn't have to try any more? Did you get fat when you were very young? Because mother forced you to eat? Only you know the answer. Examine your history.

3. Examine your fears very closely. Are you very often afraid that your husband will get into a car accident? Yes, it's possible, but if you're afraid of it all the time, or if you worry every minute that he has gotten into an accident and been killed, this fear may be masking your anger at him, and you may be eating to suppress the anger.

Are you afraid your husband or wife will leave you? If you're having marital problems, such a fear may be realistic; but if you're not having overt marital difficulty, it may mean that you have an unconscious wish to leave him or a wish that he will leave you, and you may be unconsciously eating because you hope fatness will drive him away.

Yes, fears are closely tied to wishes. Some fears are realistic and unaccompanied by an unconscious wish. Very many fears, however, are really wishes in disguise. Your unconscious is much more violent and concrete than your conscious mind. Your unconscious may solve your unconscious anger by killing off the offending party. You end up with a fear of his or her death, because you can't allow yourself to hold the anger consciously—or express it, I might add. So unconsciously, you wish the party dead, and consciously you fear the wish.

4. Examine your innermost wishes. If you secretly long for a college degree, you may really want a certain kind of respect and power, and you may be making an unconscious primitive concrete equation, "fat is power." Or lacking the degree, you may be frustrated in your job and may be eating out of frustration or out of anger against yourself for either dropping out of or never going to college.

If you secretly long to be married to someone else, you are either putting up a wall of fat so you can't be hurt by your present mate or using it as a defense against the longing. You get fat so no one else will be attracted to you or so you won't feel attractive and go looking. Your desire to be with someone else makes you feel guilty, and you eat.

If you long to be rich, you may be unconsciously or consciously angry at yourself and your husband for not being able to earn the kind of money you wish you had. Nearly everybody wants to be rich, but they don't eat themselves into the ground over it as some fat-persons do.

If none of these wishes applies to you, what *do* you long for that you may be eating over? The point is that behind the unfulfilled and unfulfillable wishes lurking in your unconscious mind lie emotions—anger, sadness, guilt, loneliness, fear, hatred, rage. Fat-persons eat out of any emotion, especially if it isn't conscious.

CHAPTER 5

SPECIAL
CASES

• OVER FORTY-FIVE •

I want to give some special consideration here to those people who are forty-five or older and married. If you are forty-five, or sixty-five, or seventy, and have been fat all your married life, your reasons for wanting to lose weight are somewhat different than either the teenager, the woman or man in the twenty-to-forty-five age group, or the divorced person.

What are your reasons for staying fat? It may be that you've always wanted to lose weight but never did, and it may be that some, or one, of the unconscious reasons for staying fat that we've discussed apply to you. There are also other reasons for obesity specific to this age group.

First of all, there is, after forty-five, a tendency for the amount of exercise we do to diminish. Second, there is the normal slowdown in metabolism as age increases. You may have always been thin, have continued to eat as you always did, and have started to put on weight after the menopause or, for men, after the age of forty-five.

The frequency of sexual intercourse also has a tendency to decrease, although many couples maintain a once-a-week frequency well into their seventies. (You're laughing because yours was never more than once a week for your whole married life? No wonder you're fat!) Obviously, frequency is a very individual matter. If once a week or once every other week or less was enough for you consciously, that's fine, and you may be fat for some other reason; but if it wasn't fine unconsciously, that could be a cause for your being fat.

There are only a few bodily pleasures in life. Two of them are sex and food. When sexual frequency diminishes, even in earlier years, often the tendency is to eat. Now, when men are having their first problems with either erection or ejaculation—which problems are normal—there is a tendency for the woman not to initiate sexual contact because she's afraid the husband will get upset, or for the man not to initiate it either because his desire is less sharp or because he is concerned about an occasional failure with erection or with ejaculation.

Some men of this age think that their potency would improve if they had a younger, not-fat woman, or even a younger fat-woman. The truth is that difficulty with erection, on occasion, is a normal phenomenon of aging, although it occurs rather infrequently before sixty. This is also the case with the other problem, not being able to have an orgasm every time. As one of my seventy-year-old patients put it, "When you get older, it takes longer to do it, but you can do it for longer." Around the age of fifty-five, some men find that they cannot have an ejaculation with every sexual contact. Often ejaculation itself takes a long time. Again, these are normal phenomena of aging. (I am not talking about complete loss of potency or complete inability to ejaculate.) Neither problem will for long be helped by a younger woman.

Women past the menopause often experience dryness of the vagina, which makes intercourse painful. The problem can be treated, which it should be, because painful intercourse may be one reason for diminished interest in sex. The biggest reason in this age group for diminution of sex drive, however, is depression. The incidence of depression increases with age; there is a greater tendency in older people to get depressed, thanks to both biological and psychological factors.

• LOSSES •

The biggest psychological factor in depression for most couples is the loss of the children. It's not really or necessarily a loss, but many people experience it that way. The last child has grown up and married or moved away. For men, that is not too bad, but for a woman whose whole life has revolved around the children, it can be a catastrophe. The woman suddenly feels not needed. She has nothing to do with her time. Over the years she has not developed enough interests or activities outside the home to sustain her.

If she is fat, she may be worried about seeming unattractive to her husband, although in long-established relationships this worry is less acute. The hours, particularly the daylight hours, seem empty. She gets depressed. She eats.

Businessmen or businesswomen who have gotten as far as they're going to get, and who know it, often get depressed because no matter how far they've come, their unconscious goals were higher, often competitive with those of a successful parent, and often falling short. This depression takes the form of not wanting to go to work, whereas previously work was enjoyed, if not loved. Depression is often accompanied by a sense of failure, a sense of being no good, loss of self-esteem, self-criticism and depreciation, loss of interest in other activities as well as work, loss of sexual interest, and, for a fat-person, loss of ability to enjoy or to take pleasure in much of anything except eating. Depressed thin-persons may experience diminished appetite; a fat-person always assuages any depression, any anxiety, with food.

Sometimes businessmen and women who are satisfied with the position they've attained also get fat because, as it is said, they "let themselves go." They've made it and they don't need anybody's approval. They value themselves and take pleasure in everything, including food. For these people, if they really value themselves, losing weight presents only moderate difficulty.

Successful businessmen or women may make the mistake of retiring early, before they are ready for it. They think they have so many things they always wanted to do that those things could occupy them for a lifetime. This may be true for some, but others, when it comes time to do all those things, suddenly find that they don't feel like doing them. They are already depressed.

Why are they depressed? Because successful people are always surrounded by reminders of their success. There are always people around who behave with deference toward them, making them feel as important as they truly are. When these self-esteem supports are withdrawn, their self-esteem drops somewhat, and this change is experienced as depression. In fact, one of the definitions of depression is loss of self-esteem.

Other people who are forced to retire at sixty-five or seventy are in the same boat. They were important to others, no matter how menial their jobs, and without their jobs they feel less important (wives and husbands don't count for much in this situation). At this age, a decline in our ego supports, a decline in our sense of importance to others (with no job there is also a tendency to feel less important to one's spouse), a decline in health or fitness, and a more or less natural decline in sex drive often combine to bring on depression.

Men or women who change jobs at forty-five, for whatever reason, often experience a depression involving some of the same psychodynamics. At their old jobs, if they held them for more than five years, they were known. Some people respected them. They probably had friends on the job, were important to some others, and loss of these familiar ego supports has resulted in a loss of self-esteem and a mild-to-moderate depression, depending on what the new jobs offer and whether the moves are lateral or downward.

In this age group, there is a tendency for all of us to assess or reassess the direction in which our lives are going. New goals need to be set up and the future, including the financial future, must be planned or implemented. There are often money worries, but more importantly, there is the "what am I going to do with the rest of my life?" worry. Most people don't feel these concerns that obviously, but rather experience them as depression or as feeling uneasy, bored, listless, unsure of what to do with their time, or as a sudden interest in younger men or women.

• REGRETS •

Another cause for depression is looking back on your life and not liking the way it has gone. There are the missed opportunities, the career disappointments, the deaths in the family, infidelities, divorces, long stretches of marital discord, problems with children, and so on ad infinitum. I would bet there are very few older people in the United States who are even almost satisfied with the way their lives have gone! We all entertain the feeling, at some point in our lives, of wishing we had all the experience that we have now and were twenty or thirty years younger. We all feel that we would do something differently if we were young again.

I think some regrets are normal, if they are accepted. You can't beat your head against a stone wall forever because you didn't go to college or because you turned down a football scholarship that might have gotten you into the "majors." A woman can't sit and regret having had or not having had children, or both she and her headbeating husband are destined for depression.

Perhaps one of our regrets is having been fat most of our lives and fat now. Maybe we have thought that our mate doesn't care anymore or that it's too late to be attractive. It's never too late. Secretly you know that, or at least hope it, or you wouldn't be reading this book.

• PHYSICAL AND MENTAL •

Depression often accompanies physical illness, which becomes increasingly prevalent as age increases. Obese older people are indeed higher risks for conditions such as diabetes, coronary artery disease, stroke, or high blood pressure, and they know it. This often compounds the depression that they are already experiencing, escalating it from a psychological reaction to a disease associated with obesity.

Often obese older people have given up on sex, and they've given up trying to change themselves or their mate. In a sense they've given up on life; they have resigned themselves to an impending death, unconsciously, and they are unconsciously depressed. They don't feel depressed; the depression shows up in obesity, loss of interests, loss of desire to get up and do anything, chronic fatigue—any or all of which they blame on whatever illness they have.

Why, in the face of strong medical pressure to lose weight, can't these older people lose weight? The answer lies in their underlying condition: they are depressed. In a sense, some of them may want to die to relieve their suffering. They have given up on life and on trying. Their only pleasure is eating or walking to the mailbox, and the pleasure of eating is tinged with guilt.

Am I saying that all older people are depressed? No, but very many of them are, for many reasons other than the easily recognized ones of money and health. An obese older person is even more prone to depression. For one thing, obese people of any age are more prone to depression; for another, older fat people often have diseases associated with obesity which are depressing in themselves. Moreover, some of the medicines used to treat, for example, hypertension, which is frequently associated with obesity, can actually cause a chemical depression, as can some medicines for arthritis. There are also medicines used for heart disease which can cause depression. Most important, obesity itself can be cause for regret and depression, due to poor self-image.

• THE HEALTHY BUT FAT OLDER PERSON •

Suppose you feel that you have adjusted reasonably well to increasing age. You have plenty to occupy your time, you enjoy retirement and leisure, and you have friends. You have children or grandchildren who live nearby by car or at least by telephone. You have been told by your doctor to reduce, yet you just can't seem to lose weight or keep it off.

First, check the kind of diet you are on. The number of calories may be too high. Obviously, take your level of physical activity into account. The less physical activity, the fewer calories it takes to keep you going. Next, check over the last few pages. Are you sure you haven't given up? Do you really care what you look like to your mate? How much do you care about anything?

If you say you do care, that you're not depressed, that everything is basically fine, then either you are not sticking to the diet you have, the diet has too many calories for your level of activity, or one of the previously mentioned unconscious reasons for staying fat (or a reason not mentioned) applies to you, whatever your age.

CHAPTER 6

DEPRESSION
ANXIETY
DRUGS AND DIETING

Every fat-person knows that we eat when we are depressed or anxious. Among thin-persons, it is fairly common to lose their appetite when they are in these frames of mind; only a tiny minority of fat-persons experience such a reaction.

Most fat-persons are depressed about their fatness, if not about other things. We therefore eat, in part, because we are fat, or because we are depressed about being fat. Basic to depression is the loss of self-esteem or absence of self-esteem, either almost totally or in one area. The amazing thing about fat-persons is that, for many of us, our fatness can overshadow in our minds all of our other qualities, and cause us to have low self-esteem regardless of our talents and achievements or, for that matter, the fact that one or several people love us.

The same is true in reverse. Depression or low self-esteem arising out of other areas in life can cause overeating, more fat and worsened self-esteem. It is a particularly vicious circle.

I think it is important to realize that fat-persons differ from thin-persons in a very basic way, a way that was laid down in their early childhood. To a fat-person, eating is the final common pathway to the resolution of many, if not all, emotions.

Eating "solves" or "soothes" all problems. We eat when we are sad or happy, to celebrate or to mourn, to suppress emotions, or to soothe anxiety or nervousness. We will take any occasion to eat. Thin-persons can't—literally can't—eat when they are nervous or depressed.

There is a basic difference here in the way fat-persons and thin-persons were taught to solve problems when quite young. If, when we were hurt as a child, our mother put a bandaid on the cut, told us we needn't cry anymore, and gave us a piece of cake, we got the message—food assuages sorrow. Thin-persons' mothers didn't do that very often.

It's true, of course, that the "food assuages sorrow" concept is incorporated in the mourning processes of all the major religions in the United States. There is not question but that food is used by all people, fat or thin, to celebrate, reward, offer thanks, offer love (a box of chocolates for Valentine's Day, Mother's Day, etc.), punishment (the withholding of food), and so on. It is really a very old ritual, this celebration with food— a throwback to the hunt and the feast. As fat-persons we are part of this culture, but somehow we seem physically and mentally different.

Physically, we are able to hold more food and water. Mentally, we are more prone to depression, which started our fatness, but not before we had learned to soothe our hurts, our pride, and our low self-esteem with food. I am saying that common to all of us, regardless of the unconscious reasons that caused us to become fat, is the use of food as the mitigator of experiences that lower our self-esteem, and that common to all fat-persons is lowered self-esteem which preceded our becoming fat, even if we became fat at age three; and, finally, that common to all of us is a pattern of using food to assuage these feelings of lowered self-esteem, a pattern which was learned even at age three or earlier.

To give a quick example of what I mean, a mother who does not or cannot take the time to hold the infant, which is what it really wants and why it is really crying, puts a bottle in its mouth. The feeding response soon inhibits the anxiety response which the baby originally had. The infant has learned an important lesson: food inhibits or soothes anxiety. Food has served effectively as a substitute for love or holding.

Now, as the child gets a little older and feels, even temporarily, that he or she is not loved, this causes great anxiety and is experienced as his or her not being lovable, or as a loss of self-esteem—yes, even by a three-year-old or two-year-old. If the child previously learned as an infant that the feeding response inhibits anxiety of any kind, not only hunger, then he looks to food even at the age of two to soothe his fears, his anxieties, his loss of self-esteem. So is a fat-person born or made.

Am I saying that *all* fat-persons learned that food inhibits anxiety and depression and assuages self-esteem? Yes! We may or may not have learned it in infancy, but physiologically, the nervous system that is called into play when we eat (parasympathetic) is antithetical to the nervous system (sympathetic) that is operative during nervousness. This sympathetic nervous system slows down digestive processes (it's the "knot in the stomach" for thin-persons) and makes it hard for thin-persons to eat when they are nervous. Fat-persons, however, override what would be a knot in the stomach and eat, and are relieved. Probably, if thin-persons could eat when they were nervous, they too would experience some relief of anxiety.

As yet I have not explained the separation of anxiety from depression. In childhood, as well as adulthood for that matter, loss of self-esteem (which is akin to depression) is often accompanied by acute anxiety, which makes them not so easy to separate. Food, in both a psychological and physiological sense, assuages anxiety, including the anxiety that results from lost self-love or esteem. Food also assuages lost self-esteem itself, which means that it assuages depression.

• LOVE, OH LOVE, OH CARELESS LOVE •

Depression arises from other things besides lowered self-esteem, although lowered self-esteem is a symptom of depression, and some "things" come down to low self-esteem, as we shall see. For instance, loss of love is a tremendous cause for depression. In the most extreme case, death, we have lost the love of the dead person. When somebody is angry at us, we feel that we have temporarily lost the love of that person. As children, when our parents are angry at us we are frightened. Why? Because we sense an acute loss of love.

If, because they are angry, they withhold food, we make an unconscious equation between the love they are withholding and food. Further, if we have been trained as infants to associate food with a decrease in anxiety or fear, we immediately want to eat when somebody is angry at us as adults. Most important, acute loss of love, whether a real loss or only experienced as such, is often followed by the unconscious feeling that we are unlovable, that we are so bad that we don't deserve love. This gives rise to feeling unconsciously depressed or feeling a loss of self-esteem which, in fat-persons, gives rise to hunger (hunger for love=food).

When our parents were angry at us as kids (or sometimes as adults), or when our spouse, who may unconsciously represent a parent, is angry at us, we often feel guilt as well as a loss of love. Guilt gives rise to anxiety and depression, and we are back where we started from.

People who, consciously or unconsciously, are considering an affair often feel guilt, consciously or unconsciously, whereupon they eat. Guilt is really, in a sense, being angry at yourself. It's often a combination of being angry at yourself and feeling bad about yourself, which in combination are cause for depression and eating, either one or both. Being guilty, being angry at yourself and feeling bad about yourself are causes for depression and symptoms of chemical depression for everybody, not just fat-persons. We fat-persons, however, eat when we experience the guilt and the self-anger. In fact, we eat when we experience any emotion.

• COMPULSIONS, COMPULSIONS •

Far from being the complacent, calm blobs that we appear to be to other people, most fat-persons are nervous inside, if not outside. We are filled with anxiety inside because we are generally compulsive, not just compulsive eaters. We are concerned with doing things right, getting things done, schedules, lists, etc. What happens to people who are compulsive and don't finish what they wanted to accomplish? They get anxious, and you know what anxiety leads to with fat-persons: eating.

Compulsive workers and list-makers and finishers feel bad about themselves if they do not live up to their own expectations; if they don't finish or didn't do everything on their list. This feeling, in a mild form, is simply disappointment or a resolve to finish a task the next day. Moderately compulsive people will work until 11:00 P.M. or later at the office or at home to finish. Severely compulsive fat-persons will give up and chuck the work, feel overwhelmed, and eat.

If there are unconscious expectations which cannot be fulfilled, compulsive fat-persons, no matter how hard they work, feel continuously frustrated, either consciously or unconsciously, become anxious and depressed, and cannot stop eating. The unconscious expectations often involve trying to please parents or secure the love of either parent. These expectations may have been given to us when we were three or four years old. ("When you grow up you're going to go to college. Isn't that wonderful?" "You're going to be just like Daddy or Mommy." "He reminds me of myself." "You're going to be a carpenter, just like Daddy." "You're going to have babies, just like Mommy.")

The expectation of equaling or bettering our parents drives many of us to food in later life because, no matter what we do, we can't outdo the parent of the same sex, even if we make more money, have more status or babies, etc. Why? Because the parent of the same sex had the parent of the opposite sex, whom we wanted. No matter how good, beautiful, handsome, talented, or rich we become, that fact remains. Yet our unconscious compulsion drives us to try to please either parent in our unconscious minds.

Why either parent, rather than just the parent of the opposite sex? Think about it for a moment. As children we desire the opposite-sex parent. We feel guilty about this toward the parent of the same sex and try to appease our guilt by trying to please the parent of the same sex. This often involves trying to be like the parent of the same sex. The process — again identification — is perfectly normal up to a point.

Often, our unconscious expectations of what would please our parents stay with us. Sometimes we call these feelings our standards, try to live up to them, fail, and eat. Sometimes the attempt is totally unconscious. We still try compulsively to live up to the expectations, we still fail, and we still eat. (Thinpersons experience the same sense of failure; they just don't eat to assuage it.)

The point is that by their very nature, these particular unconscious expectations cannot be fulfilled. The continuing sense of failure that results is depressing, and the fat-person will try to eat his or her way out of it. A better way out is to recognize the unconscious process for what it is, making it conscious and thereby robbing it of much of its power.

• POWER PLAYS •

Unconscious Oedipal strivings are not the only factors that make compulsive people compulsive. Very often the problem is the unconscious equation: power=control. Fat-persons may be compelled to achieve power over the most powerful parent or to protect themselves against the power of that parent. Fat is protection, and fatness-bigness is associated with power.

The fat-person may be compelled to strive for intellectual achievement. Academic degrees hold power. Very often, the first time a person is listened to in the family is when he or she has a degree. Not necessarily an advanced degree; a high school diploma may do. Status, too, is power. Sometimes it is not how much money you make but what your title is that counts, though more often it is how much money you make. The point is that some of us feel the need of the money or the status — the power — to "get on top" of one or both parents, or our mates, in order to be respected and listened to by our parents, our mates, or, quite often, our siblings. We often feel a need to be the best child of all the children, to be the most loved or favored. Sometimes there already is a favorite child in the family who the fat-person wants to outdo. For our whole lives we are unconsciously trying to outdo a sibling, more to gain the favor of the parents than to hurt the sibling. We work hard, seemingly achieve our goals, and yet are depressed and dissatisfied with ourselves. It's a no-win situation. We eat.

Sometimes the emotional climate in the house is such that no one is allowed to outshine the favorite child. In such a situation we "need" a distraction from ourselves in order to keep favor with our parents. We eat.

If we want but do not achieve power over our parents, and if we want but do not achieve more status than our parents or siblings, and if we don't know that that's what we want, then we are doomed to consider all our achievements as meaningless. We become unconsciously depressed, and we eat and we are fat.

What about fatness itself as a cause for depression? Certainly, it's depressing to be fat, but most fat-persons who are consciously depressed are depressed for reasons other than their weight. I know that you think that fat is ruining your life, that fat seems to be the basis of your marital discord, that fat is hampering your social life, and that if you weren't fat everything would be all right. No, it wouldn't, and the sooner you realize that it wouldn't, the better off you'll be.

I am saying that many things have to be improved, or at least have the hope of being improved, in order for you to lose weight and keep it off. If you are fighting with your husband, and it comes down to your not wanting to go places because you don't want to be seen in public, and he has business functions he wants to attend with you—then go. You're fat. So what? You are a person with opinions, talents, and interests. You are shy? That won't change if you lose weight. You have to get less shy in order to lose weight!

Are you fighting with your husband about money, the house, the kids, things that need to be done, and it comes down to being your fault because you do nothing but eat, "you fat slob?" Either that's an excuse, or you are really depressed and you are not doing anything; and if you're that depressed you probably should see a psychiatrist.

• EXCUSES •

Are you sure that you would have gotten a promotion if you were thin? Think again! Why weren't you promoted? I can't answer that, but I don't think it is valid to hang it on your weight. We fat-persons use our weight as a fantastic excuse for just about everything. If someone doesn't like us, it's because we're fat. If we don't get hired, it's because we're fat. If we don't bowl 200, it's because we're fat. (I bowled 200 when I weighed 200 pounds and when I weighed 125 pounds.)

We have a tendency not to be able to assess our attributes and faults accurately, and we damned well have a tendency to lie to ourselves. Let's say you're a secretary and can type 60 words per minute. Let's say you don't get hired for a job for which they say they want someone who can type 80 words per minute. You figure that if your figure were better you could have flirted with the interviewer and gotten the job. Maybe so, but you only type 60 words per minute. Why tie all your problems to your weight? To put it another way, your weight creates enough real difficulties for you. Why make it the scapegoat for everything that's wrong in your life?

Fat mothers are not bad mothers because they are fat, any more than a typist is a slower typist because she's fat nor a woman sloppy or neat because she's fat. Now, there is some truth in the idea that a formerly fat mother may command a little more respect from her children, but not much and not for long. If that's what you're looking for in getting thin, don't be surprised if it doesn't happen. This goes for husbands, too. Respect is something you command as a person, fat or thin. If your husband or wife really doesn't respect you, that won't change much when you're thin.

What has to start changing drastically before you can lose weight is your self-respect. That's right, *before* you lose weight. You have to become a person before you can lose weight, a person who has recognized his or her unconscious reasons for remaining fat, a person who can step back some distance from the fatness and recognize that he or she *is* a person — recognize, moreover, his or her positive attributes and plan to develop more of them.

Along with this, the most important change is the acceptance of being fat, even though you want to lose weight. The kind of acceptance I'm talking about goes something like this: "I have achieved my goals in life so far (or I have made realistic plans to achieve some of my goals), and my goals are realistic and not tied to unconscious expectations." If you're married, there must be a realistic appraisal of your marital situation: how much you love and are loved by the other person, whether the marriage is likely to last, etc. Most important, whether you're single or married, you need to assess what your best points are, where your interests lie, what you have to offer, who you are and what you want out of life.

If you can't come up with any positive feelings about yourself, or any goals or plans for your life, you are probably depressed. Do you continue to say you're depressed because you're fat? Ask yourself what plans you would have, what goals you would have if you were thin. Would you learn how to play tennis or golf, but you wouldn't be seen dead in shorts now so "what's the use?" Would you be able to look for a mate, whether you're married or single? Would you be able to get a better job or have more or better sex with your mate?

You see, you have plans, except all the plans are "When I get thin" plans. Do your plans now! The only exception is looking for a mate. I don't care how fat you are, get a pro and learn tennis, or golf, or any sport. I know you don't want to be seen dead in shorts. If you're that fat, who's going to look at you anyway? Is the pro going to look at you? You bet! You are paying him $25.00 an hour to look at your strokes! So what if he thinks you are fat? You are.

Accept it . . . live with it . . . be a person with it; and if you are not that fat, what's the problem? Do what you want to do. Become a person. Express your likes and dislikes to everybody. Don't always take it in the mouth (pun intended) because you're fat. If you want more sex, ask for more now. *Then* you can go on a diet. If you want a better job, assess your skills and go after it now. Then you'll love yourself more, and you'll be able to stay on a diet.

Do anything that increases your worth in your own eyes, your sense of self, your ego, your self-esteem. If you can't get a goal that's been ingrained in you by your parents out of your mind, then see what you can do to reach that goal, this time doing it with the knowledge that it is your parents' goal for you ("You should go to college"), but that you have incorporated it into yourself and that you want to attain it; or, give it up. If you're not depressed and it's true that you can't stand college or that you are not cut out for it, try to accept the fact. The goal doesn't have to be college, of course. Give up goals that you can't attain; if you can't give up the goal, either substitute an equally difficult one that you can attain, or try, consciously this time, to attain the goal.

This is all fine, you may say, if you're not depressed and you can start on a program of feeding your ego instead of your face. But what if you are depressed and you don't feel like doing any of these things?

• DOWN IN THE DUMPS •

There are basically two types of depression: neurotic depression and what I call "chemical depression." They have psychological symptoms in common, but the chemical depression has associated physical symptoms as well. The chemical depressions are well described in Nathan Kline's *From Sad to Glad* and Ron Fieve's *Moodswing*. If your depression fits the description of chemical depression that follows, I suggest you see your family doctor first, and hopefully get referred to a psychiatrist, in which case you will find the two books just mentioned very useful. For the moment, let's concentrate on neurotic depression.

Now, we all know what the feeling of depression is like. It is not describable by any other name. Most fat-persons are chronically mildly depressed, if only over being fat. As you already know, low self-esteem feels like depression. We fat-persons often have ways of further lowering our self-esteem by putting ourselves in a position to be rejected (not necessarily for our fat), thereby encouraging a mild chronical depression.

Neurotic depression derives, in part, from loss of love or felt loss of love either in the real world or unconsciously, mostly unconsciously. This loss of love could have been experienced as early as infancy or as late as adolescence.

There are other unconscious reasons for neurotic depression, all of which involve loss of self-esteem or guilt. There is the depression which comes from Oedipal wishes or from murderous wishes against one or both parents. There is the depression which comes from the unrelenting feeling of helplessness and dependency on the part of a child who is never allowed to be independent and self-reliant. This is really the same thing as guilt for murderous wishes, because that's what results from enforced dependency. Nothing stimulates rage like dependency and helplessness, which may explain why so many children go into so many rages.

In the case of depression that is rooted in a loss of love or felt loss of love at an early age, the "lost" love was usually the parents'. The child's reaction is usually one of feeling guilty and feeling angry at himself. (When we're depressed, whatever our age, we are very frequently guilty and angry at ourselves, often over the fact that we are depressed.) The young child has no sense of time, so that when a parent is angry the child feels that he or she has lost the parent's love forever. At that moment, the child is depressed.

Of course, renewed demonstrations of love ameliorate most of the feelings of loss, but these feelings are remembered unconsciously. The unconscious feeling most sharply remembered is the feeling of anger toward the self when mother is angry at us. This particular memory constitutes an unconscious mechanism in a neurotic depressive, and it is reactivated—the mechanism goes into effect—whenever we are rejected. Unconscious anger against the self is one cause of neurotic depression, but it is also a symptom of depression, either chemical or neurotic. In fact, when we suffer from depression of either type, we feel that we are generally substandard, no good, bad parents, bad workers, etc. This lack of self-esteem, in fat-persons, leads to overeating.

Lack of self-esteem, anger at the self, and guilt, then are symptoms of depression as well as causes for depression. More symptoms are loss of interests, loss of drives, fatigue, irritability, nervousness, anxiety, loss of ability to derive pleasure from anything, loss of energy and initiative, loss of will power (not only for where food is concerned), loss of desire to do anything, overconcern with bodily aches and pains, running from doctor to doctor even though you have been told "nothing is wrong."

Then there are the chemical symptoms: loss of sleep in a special sense (waking up two or more hours early, waking up intermittently, or sleeping more than nine hours a day, including naps), constipation, increased appetite for most fat-persons (for most thin-persons, the symptom is decreased appetite), loss of sex drive (a symptom which also occurs in neurotic depression), and a peculiar reversal of the usual mood cycle. Most people are "up" in the morning and fatigued or subdued in the evening. Depressed people feel worst in the morning and a little better in the evening.

This cycle is not the same as that of "night people," those people who prefer to sleep late and are most productive in the evening. "Night people" usually are not depressed when they get up. Depressed people sometimes wake up crying and are then at their most depressed. A classic sleep disorder of early-morning awakening consistently over a period of at least two weeks, along with the mental symptoms of depression, is enough evidence to at least suggest a probability of chemical depression in a person.

The term "chemical depression" derives from a growing body of evidence that depression is associated with an imbalance of certain chemicals in the brain. Some or all of these chemicals — norepinephrine, serotonin, dopamine, and acetylcholine — seem to be responsible for the maintenance of mood. Drugs which have been proven to affect chemical levels in the brain also alter mood, either up or down, depending on the drug.

If you have a sleep disorder, either early-morning awakening or intermittent awakening in combination with any other of the mental or physical symptoms just listed, and if the combination lasts for at least two weeks, first see your family doctor for a thorough physical, including blood work. Either your doctor or a psychiatrist can prescribe the right antidepressant to rid you of your chemical depression.

But watch out. If you are a fat-person, you are prone to being neurotically depressed or fat-depressed, as I call it (depressed because you are fat). Anti-depressant drugs will not relieve this depression, and they will increase your appetite. Nonetheless, because they relieve chemical depression, they are indicated when chemical depression is diagnosed. Why? Because nothing else will relieve a chemical depression, which can last two years or more before it relieves itself.

The sadness experienced while mourning a loss of love following death or divorce is not the same thing as depression. In mourning, you feel sad, blue, and obsessed with the loved one that has been lost. You have many of the psychological symptoms of depression, such as loss of desire to do anything and loss of ability to experience pleasure. What is missing? In mourning there is no self-hatred, no anger against the self, and no loss of self-esteem, although there may be guilt and regrets.

In mourning, the concentration is mostly on the other person, although there is also the "What's going to happen to me now?" feeling. Mourning is sorrow about the lost loved one. Depression is sorrow about the self and, sometimes, a deep sorrow about a felt loss of self. Have you ever heard a depressed person say things like "I am not myself. This isn't like me. I usually want to do things. I am usually active"? Depressed people are depressed about being depressed, just as fat-persons are fat about being fat.

What do you do about being depressed, about being fat? If you are mildly depressed all the time, mostly about being fat, and you don't identify with any of the causes listed here for neurotic depression or have—or aren't aware of—other causes for the depression, then obviously you have to lose the weight. That's the simplest way out. You will have to diet while mildly depressed, which is possible, as we shall see.

What if you feel so hopeless about losing weight, are so depressed about it, that you can't go on a diet? I suggest that you are using your weight as an excuse for being depressed, that you are really depressed about other things and that your depression and inability to lose weight have a large unconscious component. If this is true, there's still a way out. You can examine your anger, your frustrated need for power, your fears of being feminine (whether you're male or female), those "parents in your mind," and all the other things mentioned so far. If none of them fit, you may need the help of a psychiatrist in identifying the source of your depression.

Suppose something of what I've said does fit, but you recognize it doesn't change the way you feel? You say, "Okay. I'm fat because I wanted power over my mother. Now what?" You need to examine that fact in today's light. Do you still want or need power over your mother? Are there other ways you are or can be powerful over her without making the unconscious equation of fatness equals power? And so on. This is really self-analysis. I believe that it can be done, and that this book can function as a starting point.

The idea is to discover, for yourself, your unconscious equation. What does fatness represent to you? Then, once you've found it, you can examine the need for it, whatever "it" may be to you, in the reality of your personal life today. If, for example, you are a woman and have identified with the idea that you may be afraid of being feminine in the sense of being helpless, you can do something more constructive than staying fat. Start by asking yourself: What would it mean *today* to be feminine in the context of my life? Let your fantasies go. You might find out some surprising things.

What I am saying now is that we fat-persons must divorce ourselves—our fears and our frustrations—from fatness. Each of us must find our own unconscious equation and nullify it. For example, fatness isn't really power. That's ancient, archaic, unconscious stuff, and we don't have to be ruled by it. Fatness does not protect us from being hurt, and if we think about it for a minute, we know it doesn't.

You *can* divorce the unconscious meaning of your fatness from the fatness itself in light of the current reality of your life. You *can* find your unconscious equation and nullify it.

• HEEBEEJEEBIES •

Fat-persons are often depressed; even more often, we are nervous inside. Why are we nervous? I have already mentioned compulsiveness. There are a host of other factors. Let's take some reasons for nervousness or anxiety that are directly related to being fat.

First of all, there is self-consciousness. The minute we are in a room with another person we think, usually consciously, but sometimes unconsciously, "I hope I don't look too fat." Let's analyze that for a moment. What is "too" fat? Too fat for what? That's easy: too fat not to be rejected. The self-consciousness really involves the conscious or unconscious fear of rejection.

Fear is almost a synonym for anxiety. The alleged difference between fear and anxiety is that fear refers to external threats and anxiety refers to internal or unconscious threats, these being unacceptable wishes which are threatening to break into consciousness. Both fear and anxiety of the type just mentioned produce conscious fear, or conscious anxiety or nervousness. Any of the aforementioned unconscious reasons for being fat are automatically causes for anxiety or depression. The depression comes in when a person becomes unconsciously mad at himself or herself. Otherwise the feeling is experienced as anxiety, which is normal anxiety in childhood but which, if carried into adulthood, can be a cause of "abnormal" anxiety and abnormal eating.

Let's take the example of the man who wants power over his father because his father was mentally or physically cruel to him. On the surface, it appears that this is the reason he wants power over his father; that he has made the unconscious equation that fat is power and fat is protection. If we dig a little deeper, we're likely to find another reason for his wanting power over his father, that, unconsciously, he wants to win his mother's affections. (I am deliberately not saying that he wants to sleep with his mother because I think that's too narrow a concept. The child wants the mother's entire attention and love, not just sex.)

This desire for his mother's love and desire to take the mother's love away from the father is accompanied by hateful or murderous feelings toward the father, guilt over these feelings, and guilt over the unconscious thoughts of wanting the mother. As you already know, guilt produces anxiety or depression when the "guilty" person gets mad at himself for the thought that produced the guilt.

A fat-person who can be described as chronically nervous may be suffering from the primeval guilt or its associated anxiety just described, or from some other unconsciously produced anxiety. Often these old anxieties are carried right into the current realities of our adult lives. Some of us, consciously or unconsciously, are still competing with one parent for the love of the other, and trying to lose the competition by being fat. Some of us married husbands or wives who emotionally resemble our opposite-sex parent, which means that in an unconscious way we have done the unthinkable, the unacceptable — we have won the competition. Unconsciously, we have married our father or our mother. Talk about anxiety!

There are other causes for anxiety, such as not attaining your goals and being constantly frustrated, especially if you really have unconscious goals that you don't know about, or being constantly angry unconsciously, a state which is experienced as anxiety. We fat-persons are really an awfully angry group, and we swallow our anger with a food chaser. Very many of us are angry at our parents for a felt loss of love and angry at ourselves

111

for being unlovable, which leads to an unconscious depression so deep that it is not felt.

What we are experiencing is unconscious anger, which is experienced consciously as anxiety. Even those people who got fat after pregnancy or during middle age and whose unconscious dynamics have been resolved still have unconscious anger at themselves, if only for being fat. This anger is often experienced as anxiety. ("I wasn't nervous all my life, just since I got fat.")

Symptoms of anxiety come in two forms: acute or chronic. Acute anxiety may be characterized by mental panic, shortness of breath and/or excessive breathing (hyperventilation), dizziness, sweating, palpitations, pain around the heart, numbness and tingling of the extremities, coldness of the extremities, faintness, nausea, or, very occasionally, vomiting.

Understandably, most people can't tolerate this state of mind and body for very long. They take a tranquilizer if they've got some handy, go to a doctor for a Valium prescription, or go to the emergency room of a hospital to get a shot of Valium or something else. The Valium will terminate the attack, but the anxiety will recur time and again until its unconscious basis is discovered.

Chronic anxiety may be manifest, not by any physical symptoms, but by chronic mental tension. Some physical symptoms which may be present, however, are teeth grinding at night, leg pains in the morning, cold hands and cold feet all the time, and a fine tremor (shaking) of the hands.

Acute anxiety attacks are notoriously "causeless," or so the patient says. The patient doesn't know what started it. He or she says, "I was just doing my usual chores," or "I was just on my way home from work." These anxiety attacks are almost always due to some unconscious thought or wish which is threatening to become conscious. In a way, the anxiety attack serves the purpose of taking the conscious mind away from thinking and making it concentrate on the physical symptoms of the attack so that the unconscious threatening thought has little chance of breaking into consciousness.

Chronic anxiety, on the other hand, can come from being fat or from unconscious reasons. As is the case with depression, it can also have a chemical cause. Some types of anxiety are almost entirely chemical in nature and are not derived from unconscious problems. How can you tell which is which?

First, you should remember that people who have chemical anxiety also have an unconscious whose psychodynamics function in the same ways as those of people without chemical anxiety. This makes it extremely difficult to separate the two types of anxiety in one person. I separate them by watching a patient's response to drugs. If he or she does not get relief from anxiety from a minor tranquilizer (Valium, Librium, Serax, Tranxene, Miltown, or Vistaril), and does get relief from a major tranquilizer (Thorazine or another phenothiazine), I assume that the anxiety is chemical in nature.

The quality and quantity of chemical anxiety is substantially different from neurotic anxiety and, in fact, few neurotics like or can adjust to phenothiazines or other major tranquilizers used to treat chemical anxiety. The quality of chemical anxiety is more encompassing and more pervasive than that of neurotic anxiety, invading every area of emotion and response. The quantity, too, is much greater, causing greater disruption in a person's life. When anxiety of this type runs too high, paranoid symptoms sometimes develop and delusions (false beliefs), or even hallucinations may occur. Then major tranquilizers are in order.

Most of us have neurotic anxiety, however, and we may make the mistake of thinking that if we take minor tranquilizers we will decrease our anxiety and be able to diet more effectively. The trouble, as with diet pills, is that we attribute our ability to lose weight to the minor tranquilizer and never experience the sense that we can do it ourselves. It's also true, of course, that minor tranquilizers do nothing to relieve the cause of neurotic anxiety.

For chemical depression and anxiety, however, drugs work very well and should be used. You can't psychoanalyze anyone out of chemical anxiety or a chemical depression.

• DRUGS FOR DEPRESSION •

There are two types of antidepressants: the tricyclics and the MAO inhibitors (see Appendix 2). Both these types of drugs increase levels of norepinephrine, serotonin, and dopamine in the brain. As I have mentioned, derangements or decreased levels of one or more of these chemicals are thought to be the cause of chemical depression. Now, if you have had a chemical depression and your appetite has already increased as a result, it will be increased further. Tricyclics are notorious for increasing appetite. Either this is experienced as a direct chemical side effect of the drugs or, as the depression improves, a person's appetite improves. For those of us who never lose our appetite even if we are suffering from a chemical depression, the tricyclics can be a disaster for our weight; but since they alleviate the depression, making it possible for us to lose the weight later, they should be taken when prescribed.

The MAO inhibitors are excellent drugs for chemical depression, and their one drawback may not be such a drawback to us fat-persons. With MAO inhibitors you can't eat cheese, drink any liquor, or eat raisins, figs, chocolate, yogurt, and a few other things. Otherwise, you get a significant rise in blood pressure, which could give you a very bad headache or even a stroke. The MAO inhibitors have fewer side effects than tricyclics, however, and they either decrease appetite or don't affect it either way. If your appetite has increased as a result of the depression, it may remain that way. MAO inhibitors may occasionally relieve certain selected neurotic depressions, but don't bet on it. Also, MAO inhibitors don't always work on every type of chemical depression. Let a psychiatrist be your guide.

● DRUGS TO RELIEVE ANXIETY ●

As I've indicated, the use of minor tranquilizers (see Appendix 1) to relieve neurotic anxiety may be justified in certain extreme cases in which a patient's functioning is seriously impaired. Minor tranquilizers are not associated with weight gain, as are major tranquilizers. However, all minor tranquilizers are potentially addictive, both psychologically and physically. This poses a problem for the fat-person who has an "addictive personality" anyway, and who very often has dependency problems.

If you can only lose weight when taking a minor tranquilizer like Valium, you may be "learning" that Valium helps you lose weight or that you can't lose weight without Valium. This belief undermines your sense of control over your own dieting. It undermines the sense that you did it by yourself, and that any time you want to you can do it again. In the long run, it undermines your self-esteem. On the other hand, it should not undermine the self-esteem of those patients whose case is extreme — who really need Valium to function, who take it without increasing the prescribed dose, and who are under the care of a doctor, preferably a psychiatrist. The fact is that anybody who can't function adequately without a minor tranquilizer *should* see a psychiatrist.

As for major tranquilizers, the people who take them have probably seen a psychiatrist, and should see one even if the tranquilizers were prescribed by a family doctor. Major tranquilizers are all fattening, but they are not addictive. They increase appetite, and they may increase weight metabolically, but this side effect has not been proven or disproven. In any case, you absolutely can lose weight even while taking major tranquilizers or antidepressants. You need a diet containing fewer calories, but it can be done, as many of my patients have proven.

• DIET PILLS •

Nearly all diet pills (see Appendix 2) are amphetamines (speed) or act as amphetamines. As such, they stimulate the nervous system in the body, the one that takes over when we are anxious or nervous. That's why the pills make you nervous. They are also potentially addictive and can actually trigger psychotic episodes.

If that doesn't inspire you to avoid diet pills like the plague, here's another reason. We fat-persons are so used to calming anxiety with food that some of us actually get hungrier when we take diet pills; but let's assume that you are really less hungry on diet pills. In this case, the use of diet pills, like the use of minor tranquilizers, undermines your sense of control over your food intake. You attribute your control, your decreased intake, to the diet pill and never gain the sense that you can do it yourself.

Even if you lose weight on diet pills, you can't keep it off. Why? Because you can't take diet pills the rest of your life, and because their appetite-inhibiting effect is likely to taper off after about two weeks. That's right: they still make you nervous, but you override the appetite-suppressant effect in two or three weeks. "But what if I need them just to get started? Just for the first two weeks?" If you need diet pills to "get you started," you are not psychologically ready to start, and if you're not psychologically ready to start, your attempt to lose weight is doomed to fail.

Diet pills are also addictive, both physically and psychologically. *Don't take them*, and *don't* let any doctor prescribe them for you. You will never lose weight and keep it off that way. In order to lose weight and keep it off, you must solve the unconscious reasons that keep it on.

• LIQUOR •

Up to now I have said nothing about the most widely used drug for anxiety and depression—alcohol. In our society, alcohol is used as a social lubricant. It makes people more talkative and less shy. It facilitates the expression of all emotions, but particularly anger and aggression. Some people also need it in order to express tenderness or love.

Alcohol is a recreational drug, the only one presently allowed by law. It's okay to get high on liquor, but not okay, in most circles, to mellow out on barbiturates (sleeping pills) or get high on Cocaine or even, in most circles, on pot. If you think about this business of getting high, it must occur to you that the vast majority of people must be low, although there are some who feel happy and want to get higher. It is interesting that a small majority of fat-persons don't like liquor at all or drink very little. The rest drink socially, and a few of us are both alcoholic and "foodaholic."

Many of the unconscious reasons for being fat pertain as well to alcoholics, who protect themselves from their feelings or their unconscious conflicts with liquor, just as fat-persons protect themselves with fat. The bottle-is-breast concept applies to both groups. It's the contents of the bottle that differ. Both groups are trying to soothe anxiety or depression via an oral route. Also, foodaholics, like alcoholics, have gone to extremes and are out of control. Don't you hate that? Other people can control themselves so easily, and we all have to suffer. Yes, we, alcoholics or foodaholics, do suffer more than "normal" people, if only because we are alcoholic or fat.

The true alcoholic will have to get sober before he or she can get thin. Various therapies are available; among them, Alcoholics Anonymous is the one with the track record. But what about the fat-person who hasn't crossed over the line into alcoholism but who drinks too much, or, for that matter, drinks at all? His or her problem is compounded, because liquor is horribly fattening.

Fortunately, work done on unconscious conflicts can help with drinking, as it does with eating. Most of the time the unconscious purpose of drinking is to suppress awareness, consciousness, of certain emotions—usually anger, fear, anxiety, and depression. The fat-person who drinks has an even sharper need to figure out who is really making him or her angry and what's causing the anxiety or depression.

Overeaters or drinkers have a problem with behavior, whether eating or drinking, and this behavior can almost be independent of the unconscious determinants. Once we learn to overeat, even if we solve our unconscious problems, we still know how to overeat or overdrink, and we are still used to it. Also, the pleasure in these activities may be increased rather than decreased once we solve our unconscious problems. (You would think that once we knew why we were doing it, all the fun would go out of it. Not necessarily. Once we know why we're doing it, we can control it, which may make it all the more fun. We are liberated. We can eat, or, if we're not alcoholics, we can drink, without fear. When food and drink are no longer tied to unconscious meanings, we are freer and we enjoy them more.)

The name of the game, then, is learning how to control the behavior, even though we cannot control the pleasure response from our particular indulgence. I am of the opinion that to control the behavior you have to work with those behaviors already learned, and the dieting method which I will explain later, binge and starve, does just that. It does not expect total control or new behaviors. Our behaviors are all much too ingrained for that.

• ALCOHOL AND DIETING •

Some diets allow alcohol in small amounts, some diets don't allow any, and one diet a few years ago allowed as much as you wanted. So what's the scoop on alcohol?

Alcohol is very rich in energy. Carbohydrates give about four calories each gram, or about 114 calories per ounce. Fat gives about nine calories per gram, or about 256 calories per ounce. Proteins also give about four to five calories per gram. Now, alcohol gives a whopping seven calories per gram, or 200 calories per pure ounce. This has to do with the way alcohol is metabolized. Despite the fact that alcohol has no carbohydrates, it acts as a super carbohydrate in the body.

You may not realize it, but most low-carbohydrate diets end up being low in calories for the most part, except to the extent that they allow alcohol. Remember, although alcohol has no carbohydrates, it has loads of calories. Drinking very much on a low-carbohydrate diet will sabotage the diet, if only because, ultimately, everything comes down to calories.

Alcohol sabotages the diet in many other ways besides its caloric content. First, it's well-known that drinking a little whets the appetite; that's why before-dinner drinks are called aperitifs. It is also well-known that drinking a little more relaxes you and your inhibitions, including your inhibitions about eating. Drinking affects your capacity to resist the foods you shouldn't have, undermining your control.

What do you do if you are accustomed to having one or two drinks before dinner, or whenever, and it would be a great hardship to give up drinking while you are dieting? I suggest that, whether you are counting carbohydrates or calories, you count calories when it comes to alcohol. Count 100 calories for each ounce of 100-proof liquor. If you want to drink on your diet, cut out enough food to match the alcohol or, with my binge and starve method, drink only on your binge day and not on your starve days. As long as you know there are some days when you can drink without guilt, you'll have less trouble not drinking on starve days.

In general, although some diets allow alcohol, I think it is a big mistake to drink while dieting, unless it's on a binge day. Even if you forget the calories involved, alcohol has bad mental effects for the dieter. It relaxes too many inhibitions and sets the stage for cheating and failure.

CHAPTER 7

BODY
IMAGE

You know, there have often been statements to the effect that inside every fat-person is a thin-person screaming to get out. Certainly, there is a desire to be thin inside every fat-person, but the fact is that inside every fat-person is a fat-person; a fat-person who, once thin, can't believe he or she is thin, a fat-person who feels fat, who still approaches the mirror with trepidation, even after he or she has been thin for two years; a fat-person who is always hungry, whose eating must always be controlled; a fat-person who still eats too fast, always, whether binging or on maintenance or even starvation, for that matter; a fat-person who still gets the urge to eat to assuage many emotions.

The fat-person inside a now-thin body has learned complete, or almost complete, control over food intake and many other aspects of his or her life, but is still a fat-person. "Once a fat-person, always (with rare exceptions) a fat-person"—this is both comforting and disconcerting. It is comforting in that you know you will still be your basic self once you're thin, that losing weight will not change you too drastically; that you will not really become a different person, even though people may say you are because of your increased self-confidence.

It is disconcerting too because many of us hope that, when we get thin, everything negative in our lives will change, and nearly all of us hope that we will be able to eat whatever we want, that our metabolism will miraculously be different somehow. Well, this doesn't happen, but many other things do change for the better more or less permanently, as long as we control our weight.

That in itself is not an unmixed blessing. Many of us—all of us, to some degree—are afraid of change. We unconsciously resist it. Why? Because we are afraid of not knowing how to respond to a new situation, to new ways of relating to ourselves and to others. We don't know how to respond to a pass made in our direction; we may not know how to respond to renewed sexual interest from our partners; and so on. Recognizing this perfectly natural fear of change for what it is, however, makes the changes themselves seem less scary.

• INSIDE OUT •

Fat is a wall that keeps others out, but it also keeps ourselves in. Fat serves the purpose of keeping our drives in check, keeping our anger in, keeping our urges in. It is a prison, but it is also security, a security blanket of fat that keeps down our fires, our passions, our hatreds, and our fears.

What if this blanket is removed? Will we be hit with a sudden rush of uncontrollable emotion? Will we be helplessly angry and frightened? Are we afraid that if we lose weight we'll go a little crazy? Will getting thin act as a release, allowing our nasty selves to spill out, or our sexual selves? Such unconscious fears are very common to fat-persons, but the result of successful dieting is more control, not less. You feel freer, more independent, and more in control of your life; and you *are*.

Some chapters back, we established that in the fat-person's unconscious, food is love. It's also often true that fat is love, or, to put it another way, that getting or staying fat is a way of loving yourself. One of my patients said that the roll of fat around her midriff made her feel "like loving arms are around me all the time." Think of all the food (as love) that went into making all that fat. That's self-love. Not only is it self-love, it's protection and company. How can we have positive feelings for such a hated thing? Very easily, if we understand its functions.

Not only is fat self-love, but, as much as we try to deny it, it is a part of our self. It is us. We may say, "I am fat," yet see ourselves as split between mind and body: "My body is fat." But people come in bodies. Our fat is part of us, and when we start to lose weight, we are starting to lose a part of us. When we have lost most of the weight we have lost not only a part of us, but the old us, our selves as we knew ourselves.

This sense of loss can be a hidden cause of mid-to-late diet depression. We think it's because the diet seems as though it will never end, but in reality it's because we have lost our self, the one we knew for so long, the one we were used to. We are mourning for the lost fat self we hated so much. We are mourning for old patterns of thinking and feeling and relating. As hated as those patterns may have been, they were familiar, and we are all afraid of change.

When I was in medical school, I had a friend, a study-buddy, who lived across the street. He was 6' 2" tall and weighed 260 pounds. I weighed 180 pounds. We used to go grocery shopping together on his Honda, a scooter, not a motorcycle. The poor Honda labored mightily and still couldn't muster more than fifteen miles an hour under our combined weight. Then, in the summer of our freshman years, he lost 60 pounds and I lost 40 pounds. Nothing seemed to have changed. We were both still in medical school; we still had our respective partners who came to see us every weekend; we still had an incredible amount of work to do. One day we got back on the scooter to go shopping. The damned thing minus our 100 combined pounds took off like a bat out of hell. My body image changed then and there.

It's not only the feelings about ourselves that change as we lose weight. Our actual physical image changes, and though the change itself is gradual, our perception of it may come quite suddenly. The usual case is that we all still feel fat when we've dieted to 10 pounds above goal. We look in the mirror, but we don't see what's reflected there. All we see is those ten pounds. We are "still fat." When we finally get down to goal we look fat to ourselves. We literally can't believe we're thin. Then, one day, we put on a piece of clothing we expect to fit, and it doesn't. Suddenly, we're thin! I realized I was thin the morning I tried on a size 14. I immediately headed out on a shopping spree for size 12s.

Sometimes our fat-body image prevents us from engaging in activities, when we're thin, that we couldn't engage in when we were fat. I always felt that my ankles were too weak to go ice skating. (In truth, my poor ankles couldn't hold up my 200 pounds on a thin blade of steel.) When I got thin I still wouldn't go ice skating, believing that my ankles were too weak. My husband had to tell me that I was now thin enough to go ice skating. I tried, and I was.

The funny thing about body image is that it is so stable. Our body image is laid down firmly when we are 12 to 14. If we are fat at that age, we somehow never forget it and tend to continue thinking of ourselves as fat, especially if we continue to be overweight. Even if we become thin as we move through adolescence, we often keep on thinking of ourselves as fat and watch our weight. If we are thin at age 12 to 14, even if we become fat later on our body image is thin, and we are more psychologically divorced from our fat than a true fat-person.

• WE CAN'T EVEN HIDE •

One of the reasons our body image stays fat even when we don't is because we have so often been reminded of it. The fat is always *there*. It's in every mirror we look into, in the faces of people who are looking at us. It's there whenever we look down, over a protruding abdomen, at the ever-present scale. If you think about it, other conditions like alcoholism or drug addiction can be hidden, not only from the public, but from the self. In no other form of self-indulgence are we so inescapably subject to public view and comment, as well as to our own.

An alcoholic can look in the mirror on a sober morning and tell himself he's really not an alcoholic because he hasn't needed a drink yet and it's 10:00 A.M. Even if he does need a drink, his condition doesn't necessarily show. The fat-person looks in the mirror and knows he is fat; he can't hide from himself and he can't hide from the public. The evidence of his lack of self-control is visible to all, and in this society lack of self-control is a terrible vice.

How many of us have felt like a criminal when we are breaking our diet in an ice cream parlor or restaurant? How many of us have felt that the waiter or the other people at our table are watching what we eat and thinking that we shouldn't be eating what we're eating? Fat shows, and we know it shows because we know we're not supposed to be eating what we're eating. We sometimes project our feelings onto the waiter or the other people at our table. This comes out as, "They think I shouldn't be eating this," when the true thought is, "I think I shouldn't be eating this." At other times we are perfectly justified in feeling that others are thinking, "That's how she got fat, eating like that"; and they can only do it because our very own, personal fat is public knowledge.

This is not really a bad thing in the end. It reminds us, after all, to stay on our diet or maintenance plan. Remember, too, that our *good* figure is also public knowledge, and private knowledge as well. We can reward ourselves by looking in the mirror.

CHAPTER 8

PREPARING
TO
DIET

If, at this point, you understand your unconscious reasons for being fat, and you understand that you can control your actions, then, whether or not you can control your fantasies and unconscious fears, you can get thin and stay thin. You are now ready to diet.

Yet dieting remains a supreme effort. It is, as I've said, the most difficult thing in the world to do, bar none. So, if dieting is such a tremendous effort, how do you prepare yourself to make that effort—especially in the face of the fact that you have made the effort before and you have not succeeded, and you now have all of your past history and bad feelings to overcome?

• THE MOST BASIC DRIVE •

To diet is to inhibit the most basic drive any of us has. There are several ways to inhibit a drive. The first way is by substitution, that is, substitution of another drive for the drive consciously held. Sex is a good example, and you might actually substitute sex for a big dinner or for nighttime snacking. That still leaves breakfast and lunch, unless you happen to have a situation in which neither party works. Then there is the problem that the fat-person may not feel too good about sex and may have a poor sex life or no sex life at all. Certainly if you're turned off from sex because of the way you feel about your body, substitution in this area is unlikely to work.

When, for a drive such as hunger, you substitute, not another drive such as sex, but rather a pleasurable activity, it is called sublimation. It's pretty close to the old "keeping busy," and the energy that feeds the activity is said to be energy sublimated from the original drive. You can make sublimation work for you. The activity you choose should be pleasurable — something creative, something you're interested in, something that takes up physical or mental energy. Even work can be pleasurable. Try engaging in one or more of these activities whenever you get hungry.

Yet, under the best of circumstances, we all experience moments when we have the urge to eat, no matter what we're doing. It is when we reach this point that we need to have conscious control over this most basic drive. The control comes easier if we start to think about the rewards of being thin.

• REWARDS OF BEING THIN •

Some of the rewards of being thin are very obvious, yet very much worth thinking about when you're trying to control the urge to eat. I'm talking about fitting into the desired size of clothing, having sex without embarrassment, being able to wear a bathing suit, feeling attractive, and never having the feeling that people are looking at you and thinking you shouldn't be eating what you're eating. A less obvious reward of being thin is not feeling guilty if you do eat something that you enjoy or that is fattening.

The extra special reward about being thin is feeling good about yourself. It's true that people have more respect for a person who has lost weight, but the bottom line is that you have more respect for yourself.

• CONTROL •

I'm assuming that, in reaching this point in this book, you've had to go through some self-analysis to understand your unconscious reasons for staying fat. I hope I have helped you do that so far. The process of self-analysis, of course, takes longer than just reading this or any book. It takes observation of yourself and your interactions with people, takes learning to see the games you are playing with yourself, your mate, your business associates, and your children.

These games often involve control, or who controls whom. For example, the person who shops for food in a sense controls what the family eats. Sometimes the preparer of the food controls, to a certain extent, how fattening the meals will be (say, frying versus boiling). Unfortunately, there are some preparers of food who want to see the fat-person stay fat. If he or she is a mate, the preparer may not want the mate to be thin because of an unconscious fear that the fat-person will have an affair or leave the mate. If the dieter is a child, the parent's unconscious Oedipal fears may be operating. He or she may unconsciously fear that the child will take away the mate's attention. I don't care what is going on unconsciously; the fat-person who wants to go on a diet must gain control of both the shopping and the preparation of his or her food.

This control doesn't necessarily mean shopping for or cooking the food. A fat man, for example, must tell his wife exactly what to get for him and how to prepare it. Furthermore, he must refuse food not prepared properly or the wrong food. That doesn't mean he becomes a tyrant and refuses to allow other foods at the table.

You know how to diet. I don't have to tell you that you must have only what you're allowed, so it doesn't matter what else is on the table. If you solve your unconscious problems, you'll have a better chance of resisting food. The point, when preparing to diet, is to get control of the shopping and the cooking of your food.

Next comes the issue of money. Again, how much would you pay to be thin? Fat people often don't dress very well. Although there are plenty of exceptions, we do tend to dress in dark colors, black or brown or navy, and that goes for men as well as women. We also tend to wear the same clothes season after season because we don't want to spend the money on ourselves. Since we are always "about to lose weight," we don't want to "waste" the money. What's really at issue is that secretly we don't feel we are really worth it, and it doesn't matter anyway because we look terrible no matter what we wear.

This is a very common problem. If you are ready to spend some money on yourself to buy clothes for yourself now (yes, now, when you're beginning a diet), then you are ready to go on a diet. You are ready to treat yourself because you are a person and because you deserve to look your best no matter what your size. If your budget is tight, you can take the clothes in as you are losing weight. Before you go on the diet, buy yourself a few items—if you have to go to a fat-person's store, do it—that make you feel as good as you can look, whatever weight you are. Wear these items while you are losing the first 20 pounds or so, and then buy some more items (not a whole wardrobe), that make you look good for that weight, and wear them while dieting away the next 20 or 30 pounds.

Does that sound expensive? How much would you pay to treat yourself well while you are losing weight? If you cannot afford to do this at least mentally, then you are not ready to go on a diet because you don't care enough about yourself. Even if you can only afford one dress or suit, buy it, no matter what your weight at the time. When you are ready to spend a little money on yourself, you are really ready to diet. Remember, dieting is the height of deprivation. You must love yourself so much that you can deprive yourself of the most basic necessity of life. That takes a great deal of self-love. If you can't buy your fat self a new suit or dress, you are again destined to be unsuccessful in your weight loss efforts.

How can you love yourself if you are fat? My answer is that you are more than just fat. You are a person with certain talents and abilities, love and vitality, and even if you don't feel all those things right now, you have them within you and they are waiting to be expressed. You deserve to look good. You deserve to feel good, even when you're fat. If you don't feel you deserve it, you are either depressed and/or can't go on a diet with any probability of success.

• EXCUSES •

We fat-persons are always afraid of outcome. We want to know the answer to the question before the question is asked. We want to be sure that we will lose weight and keep it off before we try. We can't stand anticipation, waiting, not knowing. We have an excuse waiting in case we don't make it this time, like the one about having extra fat cells that were laid down in childhood. The membranes of these fat cells may remain, but the fat inside doesn't have to.

Often, our excuse is bad eating habits. What's a bad eating habit? Eating junk food? Eating at odd times? Eating too much or too fast? That's what being fat is. We all eat junk food, we all nosh at all hours, and we all eat too much and too fast.

The best and most common excuse is, of course, "I've never been able to do it. I can't lose weight. I'm incapable of it." You

135

know the answer to that one. Unconsciously, why do you want to be fat? Solve that one and you can be thin.

Unconscious or conscious fears of being thin often sabotage a diet when we are not looking. Some of these fears, of course, are directly linked to the unconscious reasons that we have stayed fat. Fat-persons also have other fears, based more on reality, that tend to get worse as we get thinner and that come in handy as excuses. One of these fears is the fear of increased social interaction. A fat teenager may fear that he or she won't know what to talk about in social situations; a divorced person may feel the same way because he or she is in the same position as the teenager; a fat woman may fear that once she gets attractive she will run out and have an affair; and so on.

Fears of this type lose a lot of their power to undermine your diet if you recognize that most of them are fantasy fears, not realities, unless you choose to make them so. You have control of your actions. You have control of what will happen when you do get thin. You have control over the people that feed you or prepare the food for you, if you choose to exercise it. If you're outside a mental institution, you are controlling your actions every day and you can control all your actions once you lose weight.

Let's not use excuses for supposedly not being in control of a situation, when in fact we can turn it around so that we are in control. Suppose you're in the kitchen all day because you have young children. You can plan the times that you will be in the kitchen and the times that you will not be in the kitchen. Suppose your mother-in-law is making dinner for you, and you say to her, "I really can't eat this because I'm on a diet," and she says, "Sure, once in a while you can eat." You should say to her, "I think if you really want to help me, then you will understand that I really can't eat your food. It has nothing to do with you personally, so don't take my not eating it personally." The same applies to mothers of fat teenagers and anybody else who's being served food by anybody else. Remember that you *can* refuse food from anybody.

● HOW LONG WILL IT TAKE? ●

In preparing for a diet, we often think about how much time it's going to take for us to lose the weight we have to lose. As far as I'm concerned, you have the rest of your life to lose weight. If you look at it that way, and if you consider that you have the rest of your life to lose, say, 10 pounds, then you are not so pressured by wanting to lose the 10 pounds in two weeks.

On the other hand, if you've got the rest of your life to lose the weight, then why go on a diet now? The answer is that you do want to lose the weight now, and the "now" has to be realistically determined.

Most good diets average a loss of about 2½ pounds a week. That's all, and that's a fact. You may lose 10 pounds in the first two weeks, if you're fat enough and if you're on a 600-calorie diet; but as you get closer to your goal, say around the last 20 pounds, or if you start out with just 20 pounds to lose, you may lose only 1 or 2 pounds a week or even less. The general realistic average, for people who have taken weight off and kept it off, is about 2½ pounds a week.

Figure out, therefore, how much you have to lose and how long it will take you to lose it, based on an average of 2½ pounds per week. This should be of comfort, even if it will take you two years or three years (if you're very fat) to lose all the weight you have to lose. You've got the rest of your life in which to lose it, and you can, realistically, lose it in two months, or two years, or whatever length of time is the result of your calculations. Thinking along these lines strengthens your sense of control over your weight, for the choice is yours.

CHAPTER 9

CHEATING
WITHOUT
GUILT

I am recommending in the next few pages that, in order to stay on a diet, you need to go off the diet for very short periods of time, say one or two days, after you have gained some confidence in yourself by losing some weight. But, you say, isn't it true that once you've gone off you can't go back on? That's because the guilt that you have from cheating makes you eat, which makes you feel guilty, which makes you eat, and you're trapped in a perpetual cycle of cheating-guilt-cheating. It is also true, as I said before, that we are all-or-nothing people and that we find it difficult to stop our eating once it gets started.

If you plan to cheat, if you plan a binge, then the guilt is removed. You can enjoy the binge, and you will be more likely to be able to go back on the diet refreshed and ready for another three weeks of dieting. This concept is called binge-and-starve, and I use it for dieting and maintenance. You shouldn't use it until you have enough dieting behind you to make you confident that you can lose some weight, that you can diet. For most of us, this point is reached after a loss of ten pounds or so. This means that once you lose ten pounds, and at every ten-pound interval, it is perfectly acceptable to go off your diet for one or two days and go right back on it the third.

What if you feel that you can't do this, that once you break the diet routine it is too hard for you to stop eating? I would ask, how can you expect to maintain your goal weight if you can't stop eating once you've finished dieting? The binge-and-starve method of dieting prepares you for maintenance. It is a valuable exercise; try it. "Cheat" without guilt. Plan a binge, and see if you can go back on your diet.

If you prefer to diet all the way to goal without planning a binge, especially if you have only ten pounds to lose, that's fine. If you only have ten pounds to lose, you may want to binge for one day after losing five pounds. And if, like most of us, you've never been able to maintain a weight loss, you can try a binge-and-starve diet for maintenance, never allowing your weight to reach more than two pounds over goal. A warning here: Don't let this become an every-weekend affair. If you do, you will stymie your dieting forever.

• WEEKENDS •

If your scale shows a ten-pound loss on Wednesday morning, you may prefer to continue dieting for two days, postponing your binge until the weekend. Weekends seem to be particularly difficult for dieters. On weekends we generally want to let go. We want to relax, and we don't want to exercise the same kind of control over ourselves that we generally exercise in social or business situations during the week. The weekend is a particularly good time for expressing yourself physically. You can go outdoors and get exercise if the weather is okay. Even if it's not, you can at least interest yourself in activities that take your mind off food and are fun, if not as much fun as food.

But, you say, exercise makes you hungry? All right, drink. And I mean drink—a lot of low-calorie liquids like diet soda, water, iced tea or coffee or anything that has no calories. When dieting, you should always drink at least six 8-ounce glasses of water per day anyway. Liquid is all you really need after exercise because your body has an ample supply of energy and fat stores to make up for the calories burned up by the exercise, though I know the fat stores don't make up for the hunger.

Even in winter, you can go bowling on weekends. You can go to the movies or you can play indoor tennis. The idea is to concentrate on things other than food and other than deprivation. There are many physical activities that you can do indoors. At the very least, you can do some exercises that will tone up your muscles and utilize calories at the same time. Try and find some activity — it doesn't even have to be physical — that will occupy you during the weekend so that you will not be so conscious of your lack of food.

●   BINGE-AND-STARVE   ●

The problem with dieting is that you feel you will never be able to eat the way you want to eat, ever again, and you are continuously conscious of your own deprivation. Binge-and-starve offers a way of dealing with that problem, dealing with deprivation and dealing with overeating for short periods of time. You must accept the fact that you cannot overeat all the time, but that you can binge for short periods of time, and if you learn how to enjoy the binge without guilt, you will not feel so deprived when you must go back on your maintenance or regular diet.

The starvation diets range from zero calories (fasting) to about 800 calories. The balanced diets, like the Diet Club diets, have about 1,200 calories. These diets can be used with a binge-and-starve concept as long as you realize that you have to go on the diet for a week to lose the 2 pounds that you gained from binging (planned binging). Obviously, you will have learned to stop binging at plus-two pounds.

143

It is interesting that people lose weight on any diet that is right for them. Some can lose weight on 1,200 calories; others need as few as 600 calories. A binge usually has about 3,000 calories or more. A maintenance diet has about 1,500 calories. Would anyone suggest that binging followed by maintenance is bad, or is it that binging is no good? God help us, we're going to do it anyway! Let's face it, we all binge, thins and fats alike. We go to parties, weddings, any social occasion, and we overeat. Okay, we fat-persons consume more calories on a binge than thin-persons, but we're also going to binge. It is a behavior indigenous to our culture that I don't think you can change. So, if you can't change it, you can learn to live with it. Allow it for very short periods of time, enjoy it, and stop feeling guilty about it!

With the binge-and-starve system, the reward for successful weight loss (10 pounds or more) is a one-day binge. What, exactly, constitutes a binge? A binge is not eating as much as you want of whatever you want for twenty-four hours. If you're a true fat-person, that kind of eating could put on six pounds, which would be self-defeating, to say the least. A non-undermining binge is neither unplanned nor uncontrolled. You must plan it ahead of time—this can be great fun—and you must check the calorie value of everything you plan to eat on a binge day.

For most people, a planned binge that adds no more than 2 or 3 pounds will contain no more than 3,000 calories. Try it and see how much weight you gain from that number of calories. If you gain 2 or 3 pounds, that's fine. Enjoy the binge, and go right back on your diet the next day. You can, of course, adjust your binge so that you can gain 1 pound by limiting the calories to 1,500 or 2,000. Everybody is different; a 1-pound gain, for me, occurs the moment my caloric intake exceeds 1,100 calories.

How does this work? The other day I had a date to go out to dinner with another couple. I immediately requested that we all go to a fish place. I had planned to have a salad and fish, and to allow as much dressing on the salad as I wanted. On my diet I am allowed salad only once a week, but I had lost 7 vacation-gained pounds in the past two weeks, and this was a binge day for me.

Well, the restaurant offered a salad bar, not just a small salad supplied with dinner. I couldn't resist. I had three enormous salads with all kinds of dressings—I binged on salad. I estimated the caloric count of the salad dressings as at least a thousand calories, and I indeed gained 2 pounds. I did not have dessert or anything else that was off the diet, however, and my choice of fish as an entrée helped cut down the total caloric content of the meal. A wild salad binge is all I can afford—*salad*, for God's sake! That's my metabolism. You may be able to afford more or less.

That's why the first binge, after the loss of the first 10 pounds, should be planned at about 3,000 calories. Enjoy it—you deserve it. Don't let the gain worry you. You still have a net loss of 7 or 8 pounds after the binge.

What's even more important, you will have well-grounded confidence, after that initial 10-pound loss, in your ability to lose weight; and you will have at least recognized the unconscious determinants of your weight. All of this means that you will, this time, be able to go back on your diet the day after your binge.

Is it dangerous to your health to binge and starve? Well, if you figure that it takes two days to lose a pound on a starvation diet (you can lose one pound a day for a short while), the most anybody could do is binge one day and starve one day, which would be absolutely crazy and wouldn't work. Why? Because 3,000 or more calories is likely to put on 2 pounds, and then it would take two or three days of starvation dieting to lose the 2 pounds; but dieting enough to lose 10 pounds, then having a planned binge for one or two days and then dieting again long enough to lose another 10 pounds is about the best you could hope for.

I don't know of any long-range (five years or more) studies that have followed people who regularly eat 5,000 or more calories for two days and then starve it off for five or six days. That short a study period might not even give adequate information. It might be necessary to study subjects until they die, which may be why such a study has not been undertaken. It has never been proven that binging and starving are damaging to your health. The idea just sounds bad.

Actually, what I'm talking about, at worst, is one pound down, one pound up, every other day. Thin people eat more some days and less some days, and many vary a half a pound up and down every two days or so, depending on what they've eaten. They are not static, and neither are we, but we have wider fluctuations for fewer amounts of calories. My point is: We are going to binge anyway. Let's plan it, enjoy it, and go back on our diets.

Which way would you rather have it? A shorter life span, at worst (and damage from binging and starving has not been proven), but being thin, or a shorter life span from binging and being fat?

Even if all the psychological problems are solved, the behavior still exists, and behavior modification programs don't seem able to make a dent in it. You heard a lot about behavior modification awhile ago, and now you don't hear so much about it. The reason is that behavior modification programs are like a diet: we fat-persons can't stick to them. We go through these programs and "learn" to eat slowly and put our forks down in between each bite and keep a record of what we eat, but soon we go right back to our old eating habits. My theory is that these eating habits are too deeply ingrained. Although they can be changed by one of the behavior modification programs, it takes continuing effort to keep them changed. And even then, we still go on binges.

It's interesting that when you lose weight using the binge-and-starve concept, the binges get smaller as you get thinner. You like yourself more. When it comes to a huge binge, you just can't do that to yourself. My binges have changed from putting away whole large pizzas, which are about 4,000 calories, to enjoying 2,000 carefully chosen calories. You see, the concept I'm advocating is planned binges, never uncontrolled binges, although we are all prone to those. You know, it's a funny thing. Even if you get into an unplanned, seemingly uncontrolled binge, you can exert some control. You can think for 20 seconds about what you'd like to eat and eat only that. You can have anything you want, but only that, and enjoy it. If you lose your control one day, you can even enjoy that, so long as you have learned that you can lose weight, that you know how, and that you are capable of exercising control in any moment other than the present one.

CHAPTER 10

TEN
POUNDS
TO GO

I think practically everybody in the country is trying to lose 10 pounds. A person who's 10 pounds overweight may try for years to take this small amount off, and a person who has successfully lost 60 pounds or more may find that last ten virtually impossible to get rid of. What makes it so difficult? For one thing, the person with only 10 pounds to lose doesn't really feel fat or look fat and doesn't have much motivation to go on a diet. Fat-persons who have just lost a lot of weight may be sick of their diet. As for fat people who have been 10 pounds overweight for many years, they may or may not have unconscious motivations for staying where they are. They may be playing both ends against the middle, appeasing their unconscious problems by staying just slightly fat, yet remaining thin enough to consider themselves fairly attractive.

Let's face it. It's just plain difficult to lose weight, any amount of weight, and especially a "mere" 10 pounds. The person who is 10 pounds overweight may have lost the 10 pounds many times and had them constantly creep back. If you have been able to lose 10 pounds and don't want them to creep back, I recommend that you allow 2 pounds only to creep back and then immediately go back on a diet. This means that you must weigh yourself every day. Once you have found the diet that enables you to lose weight most quickly, you know that if you do put on 2 pounds, you must immediately go on that diet and stay on it until the 2 pounds are gone.

Why 2 pounds rather than 1 pound? Because fluctuations of 1 pound can usually be attributed to water gain or loss and are generally so transient as not to be significant. Most of us, of course, can gain 2 pounds in one day, much of which is water, very easily, but if you don't go right back on your diet, those two pounds will stick.

If you have 10 pounds to lose, you cannot figure on losing more than 2, maybe 2½, pounds a week at the most, and some people, particularly those who are 5'2" tall or less, will not lose more than 1 pound a week; but don't give up. You have the rest of your life to lose the 1 pound per week, and if you can't stay on a diet for more than one week at a time, but you're able to maintain in between without gaining back your pound, then eventually you will lose the 10 pounds. If it takes you ten or twenty weeks, so what?

What if you can't stay on a starvation diet, even for one day? You just cannot not eat. Then you have to realize that you cannot allow yourself, once you get down to goal, to gain more than 1 pound. Why? Because most diets that are not starvation diets are around 1,000 calories, maybe 1,200 calories (like the Weight Watchers'), and losing 1 pound may take two, three or four days. Yes, I did say that 1 pound was most likely water, but I also said that it sticks if you don't go right back on the diet. This is especially true if you are 5'2" or less.

Let's lay to rest once and for all the myth that says losing weight is easy and keeping it off is the problem. I will say, again, that losing weight is the most difficult thing in the world to do, and that keeping it off is only slightly less difficult.

One of the pitfalls people with 10 pounds to lose get into is the idea that they have it all in their hips (or their waist or their shoulders or their thighs), and how do they know if they are going to lose the weight there? The answer is very simple. The fact is that the body will use up the fat wherever it has been stored, which means that fat areas will lose fat. But won't you also lose fat in other areas, where you don't want to lose it? Yes, you will lose fat wherever you have fat, including your breast tissues; but if you feel fat and you're 10 pounds overweight and you carry most of the 10 pounds in, say, your hips, then you're going to lose most of it in your hips. Don't use this as an excuse for not going on a diet.

Another pitfall, particularly for people who have lost 40 pounds or more, is going on a binge (obviously an unplanned binge) that takes them up 5 or 10 pounds. If you happen to go on a binge that could take you up that many pounds, then try and stop the binge at the minimum amount of gain. That's obvious, isn't it? But people say to themselves very often, "Well, if I lost 50 pounds I can lose 10 pounds in no time flat," and then they find themselves having an extremely difficult time doing it.

How do you determine whether or not you really should lose the 10 pounds? You can roughly evaluate your weight according to the following scale: A woman of 5 feet should weigh 100 pounds. A woman who is 5'1" should weigh 105 pounds, 5'2"-110, 5'3"-115, and so on. In other words, it is about 5 pounds per inch over 5 feet (100 pounds). For men, it is about 5 pounds per inch over 120 pounds at 5 feet. A man who is 5'1" should weigh 125 pounds, 5'2"-130, and so on, so that a 5'10" man weighs 170 pounds.

A 5'6" woman "should" weigh 130 pounds, but suppose you're a 5'6" woman and you say you look and feel fat at 130 pounds? Then you should evaluate whether or not you want to make the supreme effort, and I mean supreme effort, that it takes to lose, say, 10 pounds. You should also evaluate whether or not, in the past, you have ever been able to maintain a weight of 120 pounds on as few calories as it takes to maintain a weight that is probably 10 pounds less than your body likes to stay at. You may feel that you're fat and, in fact, you may be slightly fat at the weight given by these guidelines, but the problem is that to maintain anything less requires a constant supreme effort. Perhaps, after all, you can accept yourself as what you think is slightly fat, at the guideline weight.

If you can't, if you really feel, for instance, that you can't wear a bikini because you look "fat" at that weight, then try to lose the weight. The best way to lose that 10 pounds is to go on one of the starvation diets. Yes, go on a starvation diet, lose the damn weight, and then see if you can maintain it. My suggestion for maintaining it is planned binging, followed by a return to the starvation diet for as long as it takes to lose the weight from the binge, followed by three weeks of maintenance. I'll be talking more about maintenance later. For now, I'd just like to mention that for most people the best maintenance diets are the diet club diets, not the diet club maintenance programs.

Planned binges don't have to be big binges. If you're down at your goal weight, try writing down what you want to eat for one or two days, which may not be a large binge, and go ahead and eat it. Then, if you have gained a pound or two, *immediately* go back on a starvation diet for two days or so. Once you have used the starvation diet for dieting, you have at your disposal the ability to lose weight very rapidly. This allows you some flexibility in planning your maintenance or binge days.

What about getting sick from a starvation diet? It can happen, but for the most part these are temporary "sicknesses" which can be easily rectified. The sickness is generally caused by ketosis, which is not as complicated as you may have been led to believe. When fat is burned in the body, the chemical products of that fat are called ketone bodies, or just "ketones." These ketones are of no danger to anyone, providing that a person maintains a high water intake while on any diet, particularly a starvation diet. This is to protect the kidney.

Ketones make your breath bad, and sometimes they make you nauseated, which is why people say they get sick from a starvation diet. The idea that people get weak and tired and dizzy and so on is probably psychological, although occasionally it can be physical. Higher calorie diets tend to produce less of this type of sickness than starvation diets. One of my patients, who insisted she had ten pounds to lose—she was a size seven and she wanted to lose to a size five, because that's what all her clothes were—asked me to put her on my personal starvation diet. She lost 4 pounds in four days and then started getting vomitously ill, which I knew was from ketosis. I told her to eat a piece of bread, and 30 minutes later she was fine.

Diets don't really make you sick except, as I have said, on a very temporary basis, providing you were in good health before you started the diet. Obviously, every person who wants to go on a diet should first see the family physician for a checkup to make sure that he or she can tolerate even a nonstarvation diet. If you're on a starvation diet and you feel nauseous or have a headache or feel dizzy, then eat a piece of bread. Don't go on a binge, just eat a piece of bread. If that doesn't take care of it, eat another piece of bread, and if that doesn't take care of it, consult your doctor. If your doctor is unable to diagnose the problem, it may be physiological, or maybe you should try a different diet.

There are diets much more balanced than starvation diets which lose weight more slowly, such as Take Off Pounds Sensibly or Weight Watchers or variations of these diets. Even an 800-calorie starvation diet can be balanced. It is not necessary to have an all-protein diet or an all-vegetable diet or an all-egg diet or an all-anything diet in order to take off weight. As I've said, most diets that enable people to lose weight and keep it off will work at an average of 2½ pounds a week. This means that, in the long run, starvation diets do not have a significant advantage over the more balanced diets. The only real advantage of a starvation diet is that it takes off weight very rapidly in the beginning. That's why, if you have only 10 pounds to lose, I suggest that you take it off with a starvation diet, and then try to maintain it with a planned mild binge once every three days

155

or so and a maintenance diet in between. Make up your own maintenance diet, if you want. There is no magic diet. The magic is in your mind.

CHAPTER 11

STAYING
ON
THE DIET

The first thing is to avoid saying to yourself, "My God, I have 30 pounds to lose!" You have 1 pound to lose. All of us have dieted and all of us have lost weight on some diet or other. Therefore, you know how to diet, you know how to lose weight, and you know you can lose 1 pound. You can say to yourself, if you want, that after each 1 pound, or at any point in the diet, you can go on a binge and gain some of it back if you really want to. I don't think you really want to do that. The "I have only 1 pound to lose" idea is useful for successive pounds until you get to your binge day, the first one of which should come only after you have lost your first 10 pounds, or after 5 pounds if you have only 10 pounds to lose. Whichever the case, you do only have 1 pound to lose at a time.

What keeps so many of us from staying on a diet? Self-hatred, perfectionism, and negativity. These three attitudes are combined as follows: You go on a diet for two weeks, you're sure in your mind that you're perfect on the diet, and in reality you lose, let's say, 10 pounds. You then go off the diet for one day without planning it and say you've blown it. You figure that if you blew it in the morning, you might as well blow it in the afternoon and you might as well blow it the next day, and there goes the diet.

This attitude is accompanied by severe negativity ("I can't. It's obvious. I can't stay on a diet.") It can be countered by saying to yourself, "Okay, I went off the diet for one day and I didn't lose too much ground, and now I can diet again. I have the rest of my life to lose the weight." This goes for in between meals as well as the meals themselves, which means that if you go off the diet during a meal, you can and should immediately go back on the diet at some point during that meal.

Let's say you're on an all-protein diet and you have a salad. In this case, a measly salad is cheating. You should go right back on the diet by having some more protein, even if the protein itself is "extra." Or, if you're on an all-protein diet and you've had your allowance for the day and you're severely hungry, then have a piece of cheese. That way, you can pat yourself on the back and say to yourself that at least you didn't have any carbohydrates and at least you didn't go hog wild. That way, you can be positive, not negative, about what you ate.

Another very important tip is to concentrate on what you *are* allowed. Try to enjoy not only the taste but the texture of the food; whether it's tart or sweet, liquid or solid. Shift the focus of your attention from your stomach to your mouth. No matter how much we think we enjoy eating, fat-persons seldom eat for the sake of the taste. We eat so fast that we could not possibly enjoy the taste; what we enjoy is the full feeling in our stomachs. Retraining yourself to eat more slowly is unlikely to succeed for long, if at all, but this full feeling in the stomach can actually be transferred to the enjoyment of sensations in the mouth, which accomplishes the same thing.

Masters and Johnson developed the concept of sensate focus, which is basically the idea of concentrating on physical sensations that are stirring in your own body as well as coming to you from someone else. I'm suggesting that food become the focus of sensate focus, and that it be enjoyed and concentrated on during the meal. When you eat, try to think about the food you're eating and when you're eating, don't do anything else at the same time. Don't watch T.V. or read. If you do, you will find that your food is eaten even faster, that you have not enjoyed it, and that, in fact, you feel hungry after the meal. We sometimes feel hungry if we have had a long conversation during dinner or if our mind has been occupied in some other way, not because talking uses up so much energy that we need more food, but because we are not concentrating on the food at hand.

The object of this game is to concentrate on what you are allowed and not on what you are not allowed. For a moment try to concentrate hard on not eating. What comes into your mind? Food, of course, food you would like. If you try hard to concentrate on not eating, you want to eat more. If you try to concentrate on eating what you are allowed and enjoying it, you may want to eat less, which means you've got a better chance of staying on your diet.

• DOS AND DON'TS •

1. *Don't eat in any other place in the house but at the table that is used customarily for eating*

This includes not eating while standing up at the stove and picking. I had a habit of taking my first bite of food on the way over from the stove to the table, for example. We all have a tendency to cheat standing up in front of the open refrigerator. It's a way of hiding from ourselves — we are denying to ourselves that we ate anything. (Worse, we eat even faster than usual, so that nobody in the house catches us.) This means that, if we cheat, we should sit down at the table and cheat. It makes the eating, the cheating, real for us; we can't deny it as easily. On your binge day, eat everything while sitting at the table. It's more satiating that way. As for eating in front of the T.V., don't do it. You can't concentrate on the food that way. Its psychological value for you is lost, whether you're cheating or sticking to your diet.

2. *Don't talk while you're eating*

We all eat so fast that any of us can polish off a whole diet dinner in five or ten minutes, often less. This leaves plenty of non-eating time, while still at the table, for conversation. If someone is talking to you, you can put down your fork and answer them in between bites. Further, you can concentrate on the food in between sentences. Remember, conversation doesn't have to be on the menu. Don't be afraid of silence at a meal, either in the home or when you're eating out. You needn't fear that your dinner partner will think you have nothing to say. You'll make up for the five minutes or ten of silence after you've finished eating.

3. *Do drink enormous quantities of any calorie-free liquid that appeals to you*

Iced tea, coffee, non-caffeinated coffee, diet soda, club soda, mineral water, or water. How much? Well, try 8 ounces per hour. Don't worry, your kidneys can handle it. No, you won't gain weight, except the first day, maybe.

4. *Do weigh yourself every day*

Weigh yourself naked, in the morning, after urinating. Weighing yourself every day helps your control. If you're down even half a pound, you feel encouraged. If you're up even half a pound, even if it's actually water, you feel determined. Be careful not to allow weighing yourself to undermine your diet. Suppose you are good for a day and you lose a pound. The next day you are just as good and the scale says no loss. At that point you might feel discouraged instead of determined. ("You see, I was perfect and I didn't lose weight, even on this diet.") When that happens, there is a feeling of wanting to eat. Instead, you should feel like you have money in the bank: If you really are good, the weight will come off.

This is especially true for people on starvation diets who want to lose a pound a day and are ready to chuck the diet if they don't lose that pound. We fat-persons will use any excuse to chuck the diet. Worse, if you weigh 1 pound less, you may sometimes get the urge to eat because you lost the pound. Be on guard against these negative ways of reacting to gain or loss. Also, weigh every day. If you only weigh once a week, you either miss the fun of watching yourself lose weight or, if you cheated, you miss the feedback.

5. *Don't expect to be perfect*

Never start a diet saying "This time I'm not going to cheat, not once!" If you do, you're likely to use not being perfect as an excuse to chuck the diet. I wasn't perfect on my diet, and yet I lost 72 pounds. There are some days, especially when you are unusually tired, or when some big event takes place, when you are going to cheat. Don't let the fact of not being perfect make you feel so bad about yourself, so guilty, that it leads you to cheat more. The mental cycle goes: "I cheated. I am no good. I can never lose weight. I can never keep it off. I've cheated, so I might as well blow the whole day or blow two days. I ruined the diet."

The mental cycle can go another way: "I cheated, and it was good. I liked it. I did the best I could. It's time to go back on the diet!" That's the attitude that will help you get weight off and keep it off!

6. *Cheat positively*

There are moments when you think you will never lose weight, because you cannot hold out against the urge to eat for one more minute. Notice I said "the urge to eat," not "hunger," because, for the most part, most of the time, the problem is not that we are hungry. Our urge to eat derives primarily from unconscious processes. We all eat, as you know, when we feel depressed, or anxious, or angry, or tired. Whatever its source, when the urge to eat is so strong that you cannot resist it for one more minute, take 20 seconds or so to plan what you're going to eat. Write it down. Plan something good, enjoy eating it, and remember that you have the rest of your life to lose weight; and that you *can* and *do* lose it when you're not in a sudden, binging frame of mind. That's being positive.

It's also important, of course, to contain the cheating to amounts as small as possible. If you have to cheat, cheat protein. Cheat on cheese, meat, fish or poultry, but try not to cheat on carbohydrates or fats. Have an egg. An egg is only 100 calories, mostly protein, some fat, and almost no carbohydrates.

7. *Plan to cheat*

Starting a diet and expecting to be perfect all the way through is what defeated you in the past. That's why I have suggested that you plan to cheat. Decide that after three weeks of dieting you're going to have a one-day binge. Go ahead and have your binge, and enjoy it. Do not feel guilty. You have not blown your diet, which you'll be going right back on the next day.

Planned cheating allows you more energy for dieting until the next cheating period. (We really shouldn't even call it cheating. We should call it planned binging, or planned overeating, or a planned vacation from the diet.) This type of dieting also prepares you for maintenance, during which you will be allowed to eat what you want for several days in a row, only to go back on the diet later.

Frankly, I don't think that this type of program makes dieting really much easier. In some ways, it makes it more difficult. This is because we are all "all-or-nothing" people, I-can't-stop-the-response people. It is very difficult for us to stop our eating responses, as any fat-person who has ever tried to leave half a serving of ice cream on his plate knows. I do believe, however, that this type of program makes dieting possible—makes dieting down to goal possible for those people who have never been able to do it before.

What if you have not planned a binge, and you come upon a sudden and short-lived period during which you feel you must go off the diet? There are several things you can do. If you're at home, get out of the kitchen. If you're dining out, go to the bathroom of the restaurant.

What if you've planned a binge and you come to the binge day and you don't feel like binging? Terrific! Don't binge; stay on your diet and save yourself a pound or two. If you've planned a binge and you do feel like binging, make sure you go ahead and enjoy it. Give yourself a pat on the back. Even if you cheated by eating more than you wrote down, say to yourself that it could have been worse and that you could have cheated more. The same applies to cheating when you didn't plan a binge, which is really cheating. However much you ate, you certainly could have eaten more. Say to yourself that you did the best you could and that you will do better in the morning.

What I am suggesting is that you think positively while you're dieting. Weigh yourself every day and concentrate on the fact that you lost a half a pound, not the fact that you didn't lose a whole pound. Even if you cheated, at least you didn't gain, or, if you did gain, you could have gained even more. If you go off the diet, go right back on. If you've cheated all day long and you still have your 8 ounces of protein for the day to eat at night, then eat it. Don't skip it. It tells you that you're going back on the diet, besides which, you're entitled to it. Think positively!

CHAPTER 12

OTHER
PEOPLE

You already know that other people try and stop us from losing weight. Sometimes the attempt is quite obvious; sometimes it is subtle. Occasionally, if I want to lose 4 pounds in two days, I fast. That's not dangerous, fasting for two days—but my own husband tries to give me food during this period. Now, what can possess him and other husbands or wives or mothers to do something like this? When you deliberately leave some food on a plate, they say, "Is that all you're eating?" or "Are you leaving that, Honey?" What lies behind remarks like that?

Keep in mind that the people surrounding us may have their fantasies and fears regarding our weight loss. The most obvious situation is the one in which partners are afraid that we will become attracted and attractive to someone else. They are afraid that they will lose us, or, at least, that they will lose their control over us, that we won't be so dependent on them. Why? Because thinness breeds independence, just as fatness breeds dependency. If we are thin, we have more self-confidence, and we know that we are capable of attracting a new partner.

Moreover, we know that we are attractive to the old partner, and this gives us the self-confidence to stand up to the partner without as much unconscious fear of losing them or as much fear of their anger. The partner reacts to the weight loss with an unconscious fear of loss of control of the relationship.

Before a fat-person can lose weight, he or she may be subject to the subterfuges of a mate or a parent. Let's take the example of a mother and a fat child. She may have reverse Oedipal feelings and unconsciously fear that her fat daughter will, if she becomes thin, attract the love and attention of the father. This comes out as refusing to bar candy and other junk food from the house on the grounds that it would deprive the other children of their snacks, knowing that the fat child can't resist these things if they are in the house. This is a poor excuse, especially if she also knows, as most of us do, that nobody needs junk food. The mother of a fat adolescent son may sabotage his attempt to diet in this or some other way, unconsciously fearing that she will no longer be the apple of his eye once he feels he can attract girls.

Parents may also fear their adolescent child's getting into sex for unconscious reasons, not just the conscious factor of parental concern. A child's having sex marks the end of his or her childhood and may remind mothers or fathers of their own aging process. They don't want the child to grow up too fast. The child's getting thin not only increases the likelihood of sexual involvement, but also means growing up to the parent. To both parent and child, it means that the child has readied himself or herself to hunt for a mate. It also means that he or she is less dependent on the parent, and the parent may unconsciously fear the loss or changing of that dependent relationship.

Mates can be subtle, playing on the guilt of the fat-person. One husband I know, when his wife was fat, used to leave the usual amount of food on his plate. He was genuinely full. Invariably, she would finish her own meal and what was left of his. When she went on a diet, he would say, "Here, Honey, you want to finish this," and, the zinger, "it's a shame to waste it. You gave me too much." The wife's variation on this game, when she wasn't dieting, was to overfill his plate so that she could have the leftovers. Now, it is a very subtle game that both were playing. It's hard for the fat-person to stop—we all have this thing about not wasting food—but the impulse to go on eating can and should be stopped. Recognizing what's really going on will help. Even more important, recognizing that you can have control over the situation and decide once and for all that you will not eat anything left on someone else's plate.

I am not saying that all husbands and wives are going to undermine the fat-person's dieting. Quite the contrary. Some mates are very turned off by the lack of control exhibited by some fat-persons before dieting. They really don't have an unconscious need to keep the fat-person fat. Nonetheless, they can get sucked into feeling sorry for us during a diet and may offer us food. They can also get sucked into the games we play, especially our game of "I need your help to diet. Don't let me eat!" In order to diet successfully, the fat-person must be in full control, always, except in certain instances. When you are eating something forbidden and you ask your mate "Take this away from me" or "Don't give that to me." Otherwise, you're on your own.

Mates, whether or not they really want you to lose weight, should not be put in the position of watchdog. You shouldn't feel that you can't cheat in front of them. If you're going to cheat, you're going to cheat, and it should not matter to them. You shouldn't feel that you have to eat those Mallomars in the bathroom.

Be wary of the following remarks: "You can have just one, can't you?" "You can have it just this once, can't you?" "One drink can't hurt you, it only has 150 calories." "It's Johnny's birthday—it only comes once a year." "You can have a little bit of everything." "A little bit won't hurt you." "I can eat just one portion, why can't you?" "If you're so irritable from dieting, why don't you eat something?" And, especially for the 10-pound-overweight person: "You look okay to me. Why do you have to lose weight?" "You're not fat." "I love you as you are." "I like you slightly chubby." "You're the thinnest one in the crowd." "I can't stand to see you suffer over a lousy 10 pounds."

These remarks, and others like them, are often said by mates who unconsciously fear their partner's losing weight, and occasionally by mates who really hate to see us suffer. Another variation of this is the mate who wants to help, who tells you to avoid certain foods, doesn't let you binge when you're supposed to, and in general tries to maintain his customary control over you.

Then there are friends, or so-called friends. One of my patients was at a get-together lunch with six friends. She weighed 240 pounds and made the mistake of telling her friends she was on a diet in order to justify her refusal to eat. (Thin people don't feel the need to justify their portions or not eating to anyone because they don't assume anybody is watching them eat. Fat-persons always assume everybody watches and cares about what they eat.) Cake was served, and my patient didn't eat any. The hostess, who was fat herself, and the other woman kept talking about how good the cake was. The hostess said to my patient, "It's too bad you couldn't have a piece of cake." My patient, who was furious by this time, said, "I hope you enjoyed yours, because you probably gained half a pound eating it." That's what you have to do. Stand up for yourself!

Remember, friends can have unconscious fantasies about us also. Unconsciously, they don't, sometimes, want us to be thin and attractive. They may fear that we will attract the attention of their mate, or that we will be better looking than they.

It is clear that other people who are involved with us, and some other people whom we see casually, can be very harmful to our dieting and to our self-esteem. Sometimes, or most of the time, these people want to help. It is often the ones closest to us that are the most inimical to us, either because they want to help or because they have unconscious fantasies about us that drive them to thwart our dieting.

You must take control of your dieting. You can't let other people interfere, even if they are very close to you. Once other people see that you are in control, they are more likely to respect you for it and allow you to do your dieting for yourself.

CHAPTER 13

CHOOSING
A
DIET

REMEMBER! THERE IS NO MAGIC DIET. THE MAGIC IS IN YOUR MIND.

• KETOSIS •

The "magic" held out by the most popular diets, year in and year out, depends on that non-magical phenomenon of ketosis.

When fat is broken down in the body, its products are called ketones. The presence of ketones in the bloodstream and, subsequently, in the urine, is called ketosis. Now, ketones, by some unknown mechanism, tend to suppress the appetite center in the brain. This is the underlying principle of all high-protein diets that do not specify the quantities of protein to be eaten. They depend on the natural suppression of the hunger center by the ketosis produced early in the diet, thanks to the intake of high-protein, low-carbohydrate foods.

There is, however, an essential flaw in all diets of whatever type that do not specify the exact amounts of food to be eaten. That flaw is their dependence on ketosis to suppress our appetites. Why? Because fat-persons do not often eat out of hunger. We don't even pay much attention to whether we are hungry or not. We eat for psychological reasons, and we overeat the ketosis induced by any diet. Fat-persons cannot depend on ketosis to avert their hunger.

It's true, nonetheless, that many people do lose some weight for awhile on high-protein diets such as Atkins or Stillman or Scarsdale, and may even experience a temporary loss of some of their appetite; but loss all the way to goal requires conscious suppression of hunger, nearly all the time, in every situation in which overeating can occur.

The Atkins, Stillman, and Scarsdale diets are basically different variations of a high-protein, low-carbohydrate, low-fat diet, except that Atkins allows a moderate amount of fat. They are good diets as such, but they fail to specify quantities. They depend too much on the suppression of hunger induced by ketosis. Those of us who eat for psychological reasons will overeat the ketosis, and may even gain weight, on a diet that says "eat all you want of this protein" or "eat a moderate amount". What the hell is a moderate amount? All you want? I could easily eat 3 or 4 pounds of hamburger in one sitting every day! That has 6,400 calories. In no way am I going to lose weight eating 6,400 calories, no matter whether it's protein or anything else. Dr. Stillman, Dr. Atkins and Dr. Tarnower might argue that I would only do that the first day or two, that the ketosis induced would then cause me to lose my appetite, and that I would eat moderate or small amounts after the second day on the diet. I'm sorry, doctors, but I never lose my appetite, for any reason, ketosis or no ketosis; and I have been on these diets.

Diets of the Atkins, Stillman, or Scarsdale type are perhaps best for people who have gotten fat from increasing age or from pregnancy but are not true fat-persons, although they are fat now. These people may respond to a ketosis-induced loss of hunger and may be able to moderate quantities for themselves by following their real sense of hunger. True fat-persons, however, cannot depend on this mechanism. We are nearly always hungry, no matter how much we've eaten.

•   CARBOHYDRATES AND PROTEIN   •

When protein is eaten, a certain percentage of its available calories are used up in metabolic processes involving its utilization. This is called the "specific dynamic action" of protein, and is known to occur in animals and believed to occur in humans. It means, in the final analysis, that perhaps about 25 percent of the calories in a piece of protein are actually used up in utilizing the energy from the remaining 75 percent. So, by eating mostly protein on a diet of 1,000 calories, we may really be eating only 750 utilizable calories. The other 250 calories are used up in metabolic processes specific to protein. Carbohydrates and fats do not have this advantage because they do not have a specific dynamic action. That's why the best diets are high in protein; but again, for fat-persons, the quantities *must* be limited and specified.

As for carbohydrates, everybody knows you can't have too many of them while dieting. Vegetables have carbohydrates, and Atkins limits the amount of vegetables by limiting the amount of carbohydrates. Stillman says that some vegetables are unlimited, as is protein. Tarnower says that his diet "averages out" to around 1,000 calories daily, but the amounts that keep the dieter at that average are often not specified.

Whether you count carbohydrates or calories, some vegetables are okay on most diets. If Stillman, Atkins, and Tarnower were careful to specify protein amounts, then their diets would be similar in concept and content to Weight Watchers. All three are pretty well-balanced diets. If these or any other high-protein diets appeal to you, I'd suggest that you use them, but limit your amount of protein to 8 ounces per day.

•   PSYCHOLOGICAL APPEAL   •

Psychologically speaking, which diet is best for you? Any diet that says eat as much protein as you want, but limit the carbohydrates, is psychologically very attractive. We love to eat as much as we want of anything. But these diets do *not*, repeat, do *not* really come down to eating as much as you want. You might lose weight for the first day or two of eating as much protein as you want, if your previous eating pattern included a great many carbohydrates. Again, these diets depend on a ketosis-induced decrease in hunger, and true fat-persons do not respond to physiological decreases in hunger.

We hunger for more than food. Our hunger is psychological. Even if we have solved our unconscious reasons for staying fat, the urge to eat in response to emotional stimuli is still there. We can more easily control our urge to eat once we have solved our unconscious reasons for staying fat, but our hunger is still there. We just control it better.

If somebody tells us that we don't have to control our hunger and that we can eat as much as we want, his diet is bound to appeal to us. In the long run, though, since true fat-persons eat out of psychological hunger, we are doomed to failure on diets that encourage us to eat unlimited quantities of protein, whatever their limitations on carbohydrates and fats. If we did respond to the physiological stimulus they depend on (ketosis-induced lack of hunger), we would end up limiting our protein quantities. "Eat all you want" of protein is a very tricky statement—theoretically you won't want much because of the ketosis. Ah, but we do! We overeat ketosis. We overeat anything except specified quantities, and we may overeat those too!

If you go on Stillman or Atkins or Scarsdale and eat as much as you want for as long as you want, you're likely to end up discouraged and disappointed. On the other hand, if you do respond to physiological hunger-reduction, as many fat thin-persons do, you will have no trouble losing weight on Atkins or Stillman or Scarsdale. The problem is that these diets and their maintenance programs forget that there are occasions when we overeat. They seem to expect perfect control all the time, like going to a party with your little carbohydrate counter. If you've dieted close to goal, then binge a day or two, and then go back to eating as much as you want of protein. You may not lose the pound or two quickly; in fact, you may gain weight.

• ANY DIET •

For us, any diet is starvation, because we can't eat as much as we want. That's why I prefer a real starvation diet, to be followed by a short binge. Psychologically, it's best to avoid being faked out by diets that promise you can eat as much as you want of certain foods, usually protein. There are some good diets around that do state all quantities. Diet club diets, such as Weight Watchers or Take Off Pounds Sensibly, are psychologically good in that you feel you are eating in a healthy way. High fiber diets are the same. Their psychological drawback is that you lose the weight more slowly.

Starvation diets are, by necessity, largely unbalanced. They cause rapid weight loss, which is their psychological advantage. If you are in good health, your body can tolerate a starvation diet for a long period of time, providing you take supplementary vitamins, calcium, and potassium and other minerals.

Remember: In the last analysis, it is not which type of diet you go on, but whether or not you can stick to it, that matters. Sticking to a diet involves the way you diet. Any diet that is a diet can be used in the "binge-and-starve" way, with excellent results.

• RATE OF LOSS •

Another thing to be considered, in a psychological sense, is how fast you need to lose weight at the beginning of a diet in order to stay on it, and how fast you need to lose weight, period. I know everybody wants to lose it yesterday. If you use your physiological hunger as a guide on Atkins or Stillman or

Scarsdale, you will probably eat around 1,000 calories per day. This will cause a weight loss during the first two weeks of up to 5 or 10 pounds per week, although Stillman gives examples of greater loss. After the first two weeks the loss tapers to 4 or 3 pounds per week for awhile, then to 2½ pounds per week for the remainder of the diet.

The Weight Watchers diet allows 1,200 calories on most days and 1,000 calories on some days. Compared to the number of calories we eat when not dieting, 1,200 calories is few enough to produce a loss of 5 to 10 pounds in two weeks in those who begin the diet 50 pounds or more overweight, and smaller losses in those with less weight to lose. A 600-calorie starvation diet will cause a pound per day loss for the first two or three weeks of dieting. Thereafter it tapers to 5 or 3 pounds a week for the rest of the diet, if you can stay on it.

At the bitter end of most diets you only lose 1 pound per week. Now, if you add up one week of a 5 to 10 pound loss, then a loss of 3 pounds per week for ten weeks and 1 pound per week for five weeks, that comes to 42 pounds in 16 weeks, or an average of 2.62 pounds per week. So, whether you lose 2½ pounds every week or you lose 20 pounds in the first two weeks and taper off, it doesn't really matter, except psychologically. Psychologically, we seem to need to lose a lot of weight in the beginning of a diet to keep us motivated for the rest of it. My recommendation is that you start with a limited-quantity, all-protein, no-carbohydrate, no-fat, 600-800-calorie-per-day starvation diet. Psychologically, this is good to try in the beginning, even if you switch to Stillman or Atkins or Scarsdale or Weight Watchers later on.

Since to us, psychologically, any diet is starvation, if you have solved your unconscious problems or reasons for staying fat, it can be a lot of fun to go on a starvation diet and lose weight very rapidly in the beginning. If you have not solved your unconscious reasons for staying fat or if you don't think you really have any, you can try either Stillman, Atkins, Scarsdale or Weight

Watchers; but people who have unconscious reasons for being fat will not be able to stick to the diet, whichever they choose, if the reasons are still unconscious.

Which diet is psychologically right for you if they all average out to 2½ pounds per week? Well, starvation, with its very quick weight loss, is fun for the beginning. Stillman, Atkins, Scarsdale, Weight Watchers, and Fredricks' High Fiber are all balanced when they allow vegetables, and they all cause loss of about 10 percent of the amount of overweight in the first week or two, especially if you limit the protein on Stillman, Atkins and Scarsdale to 8 ounces per day. If you don't think you'll overeat the ketosis, try Stillman or Atkins or Scarsdale without limiting the protein. If this works, you'll be very psychologically pleased. Also, Stillman, Atkins, Scarsdale, Fredricks, and Weight Watchers, like any reducing diet, are, to one extent or another, high-protein, low-carbohydrate, and low-fat.

Am I saying that all diets are the same? To the extent that fats and carbohydrates are limited or very limited on all diets, yes, diets are the same. Can you eat as much as you want of protein on some diets? No, not really!—not as much as you want psychologically.

To the extent that a diet is a diet—to the extent that you must limit your intake of food, particularly carbohydrates, and fats, on any diet—all diets are the same psychologically. The best one for you, psychologically, is the one that helps you lose weight, no matter how. If ketosis works for you, fine. If you prefer to count calories, fine. In the next chapter, I will teach you how to lose weight successfully on any diet you choose.

For now, here are my suggestions to aid you in choosing a diet:

1. Remember, it doesn't matter which diet you go on so long as you lose weight on it. If the first one you choose doesn't seem right for you, try another.

2. If you are "only" 10 pounds overweight, I would recommend my starvation diet, or Stillman, limiting the quantities. Either one will get the job over with as quickly as possible.

3. If you are more than 10 pounds overweight but are basically not a fat-person, if you can't find any unconscious reasons for your overweight, and/or you do respond to ketosis, you can consider diets that limit carbohydrates rather than calories, such as Stillman, Atkins, and Scarsdale.

4. If you are a true fat-person, if you eat under the pressure of any emotion, and you recognize one or more unconscious reasons for staying fat, you may or may not respond to ketosis and you are better off not going on Stillman, Atkins, Scarsdale, or any diet that doesn't specify quantities.

I have generally discussed those diets that are currently most in use in this chapter and will discuss them specifically in the next, because these will be the most familiar to you. New diets will, of course, continue to appear. It doesn't matter, because whatever diet comes out you need concern yourself with only one distinction: does it limit quantities or not? If it's a legitimate diet and doesn't limit quantities, it will have to depend on ketosis to deaden your hunger so that you will ultimately limit the quantities yourself. If it does limit quantities, you will still develop some degree of ketosis, which will help you stay on the diet to the degree that you experience the ketosis. But remember: only you can determine whether you respond to ketosis or whether, like me, you can't limit quantities unless somebody tells you exactly how much to eat.

6. Don't forget that, whatever diet you choose, you can go off it once every 10 pounds, binge to 3,000 calories, and then go right back on the diet. "Binge-and-starve" works with any diet that loses weight for you.

CHAPTER 14

THE
DIETS
WITH
COMMENTARY

1. Allows some alcohol after the first week.
2. Allows unlimited quantities of protein (except cheese, which is limited to 4 ounces per day).
3. Allows "judicious" quantities (unspecified) of fats, oils, mayonnaise, etc., even in the first week.
4. No fruit the first week.
5. Allows moderate amounts of carbohydrates after the first week, including fruit (8-20 grams of carbohydrates per day).
6. Allows some vegetables to be added after the first week.
7. Carbohydrate intake is guided by weight loss and to some extent by one's general energy level. There are certain carbohydrate-loaded foods which are prohibited entirely.

COMMENTS: This diet is predicated on the ketosis-kills-hunger theory and may work for you all the way to goal. On the other hand, it may quit on you in Week #3 or #4. There are two reasons for this: that you start to get hungry again and psychologically override the ketosis-induced lack of hunger, and that the quantities you had in the first two weeks cause weight loss because they differ so drastically from your previous eating habits. Once you have lost some weight, you need less protein to lose than you did previously. If you continue to eat the same quantities that helped you lose weight in the beginning, you won't lose any more. Remember, Dr. Atkins is banking on ketosis to make you want less and self-limit the quantities. This may not always work.

Atkins' quantities are unspecified as to protein and fat, which is dangerous for fat-persons. One person's "judicious" amount of fat is often not the same as another person's. If, however, you choose your fruits and vegetables carefully, the Atkins diet becomes well-balanced, and if you limit your protein to 10 ounces per day, it differs only slightly from Weight Watchers.

A typical Atkins Super-Energy diet for the first week would be an unlimited quantity of protein (eat as much as you want—eggs are included), two small salads per day, and "judicious" but unspecified amounts of fat. As the weeks go by, you can add up to 20 grams per day of carbohydrates, so long as you continue to lose weight. You need a carbohydrate counter. Dr. Atkins' "diet revolution," set forth in his original book, differs little from the super-energy diet and has the same failing: no limit on protein except the limit you impose because of ketosis-suppressed hunger, or the limit you don't impose because of psychological factors overriding the ketosis.

• WEIGHT WATCHERS, TOPS, ETC. •

Weight Watchers and other diet club diets are the most balanced of all the diets. They are probably the easiest to follow and to stay on for long periods of time. I recommend them for anybody who is 30 or more pounds overweight, or who anticipates a very long dieting period. They are ideal for junk-food addicts who have to learn to eat well-balanced, healthy meals.

COMMENTS: The problem with the diet club diets is that they are so well balanced, allowing limited quantities of all carbohydrates, fats, and proteins, that they may allow too many calories for many people, especially people who have only 10 pounds to lose. People with 10 pounds or so to lose who have kept losing it and regaining it are definitely better off using a starvation (600-calorie) diet to lose the weight, and then binging and starving to maintain the loss.

Weight Watchers does specify quantities (thank heavens), does require specific foods (such as fish) to be eaten several times per week, and does prohibit eating beef more than three times per week.

Menus for a typical day on Weight Watchers might be:

Breakfast: 1 egg or 1 oz. hard cheese or 2 oz. fish or ¼ cup cottage cheese and 1 slice bread with butter

Lunch: 4 oz. fish or meat or poultry or ⅔ cup cottage cheese or pot cheese or 4 oz. farmer's cheese, 2 eggs or 2 oz. hard cheese, limited vegetables of certain types, and 1 slice bread with butter.

Dinner: 6 oz. fish or meat or poultry, and 4 oz. of certain limited vegetables.

Also allowed are three fruits per day for women and five fruits per day for men. Men are allowed two slices of bread at breakfast and lunch and 8 ounces of meat, fish, or poultry for dinner. Both men and women are allowed two glasses of skim milk per day. Bread may be substituted for by ½ cup rice or spaghetti.

COMMENTS: What I've just described amounts to a hell of a lot of food for a dieter, and in my experience Weight Watchers indeed has too many calories to work well for the 10- to 20-pound loser; but it does work for most people who are 20

pounds or more overweight. It also retrains your food habits. I recommend it for maintenance following a starvation diet. Yes, I mean the Weight Watchers diet, not the Weight Watchers maintenance program. Too many people I know have gained weight on Weight Watchers maintenance. Also, if you are coming off starvation, you're going to gain weight the first week no matter what maintenance plan you're on. Weight Watchers can be used with "binge-and-starve," but it takes longer to lose the 2 pounds that you gained from the binge.

• STILLMAN •

1. Allows some alcohol.
2. Allows unlimited quantities of protein (some proteins are preferred, such as chicken and fish over beef).
3. Allows certain vegetables.
4. Allows a little fat (very little).

Menus for a typical day on Stillman might be:

Breakfast: Unspecified quantity of lean bacon and protein, plus bun

Lunch: Beef bouillon, unspecified amount of broiled hamburger with tomato, and unspecified amount of yogurt with sugarless jam

Dinner: Small (what's that?) shrimp cocktail (with sauce?), unspecified quantity of broiled halibut, and Romaine, chicory, and escarole salad with vinegar dressing and dry white wine (unspecified quantity).

COMMENTS: If you want to go on Stillman, you'd do better on my favorite starvation diet—at least it tells you how much to eat. If you do go on Stillman, watch the alcohol. Too much (more than one regular bartender-made drink per day) and you may wreck the diet.

This diet also depends on ketosis-killed hunger to encourage you to self-limit the quantities. Beware!

• CARLTON FREDERICKS' HIGH-FIBRE DIET •

Basically, this is a limited-protein, limited-fat and carbo-hydrate diet. It is a meat, vegetable and fruit diet much like Weight Watchers, with a few bran tablets and crackers thrown in. The amounts of the items are more limited than in Weight Watchers, and in protein content the diet resembles a starvation diet (8 ounces of protein per day). It will be easier to stay on than my favorite starvation diet, will help you lose weight almost as fast, and will be less boring.

Menus for a typical day on Fredericks' might be:

Breakfast:	Unspecified quantity of fruit or fruit juice, 1 egg, unspecified quantity of plain yogurt, and 2-4 500-mg. bran tablets
Lunch:	4 oz. lean meat or fish or poultry, ½ cup cabbage (this is basically nothing), unspecified quantity of fruit, 1 glass skim milk, 2-4 500-mg. bran tablets
Dinner:	4 oz. lean meat or fish or poultry, 2 vegetables (cabbage and cauliflower), salad (1 teaspoon of any dressing to be split between the lunch salad and the dinner salad), unspecified quantity of fruit, 2-4 500-mg. bran tablets

COMMENTS: If you need the laxative effects of bran, you can take bran tablets with any diet. The bran doesn't help you lose weight. This is, however, a good variant of a starvation diet and is more well balanced.

• THE SCARSDALE DIET •

This diet is obviously aimed at the 10-pounds-to-lose dieter. Dr. Tarnower has many suggestions about staying on the diet for two weeks, off for two weeks, etc. It's even called the Scarsdale Medical 14-Day Diet. As with Atkins and Stillman, the diet does not specify quantities, depending on ketosis to limit your intake.

Menus for a typical day on Scarsdale might be:

Breakfast:	½ grapefruit or fruit in season, and 1 slice protein bread
Lunch:	Fruit salad (any combination of fruits, as much as you want)!
Dinner:	(and I quote) "plenty" of broiled lean hamburger and tomatoes, lettuce, celery, olives, brussels sprouts or cucumbers

COMMENTS: If someone says "plenty" to me, that's at least 2½ pounds of hamburger, or 4,000 calories. In no way am I or anyone else going to lose weight for long on that!

Yet many people have been temporarily successful with this diet. If you succeed on Scarsdale, you are probably 10 pounds overweight, and you are a fat/thin-person who responds to ketosis—who eats 8 ounces of meat when someone says "plenty."

Since Scarsdale really is a 14-day diet, if you can't lose all you have to lose in 14 days, you should either use Scarsdale on the two-weeks-on, two-weeks-off program or avoid the diet. Avoid it especially if you don't know what "plenty" is, if you can't limit your intake, if you get "hungry" even if you're using ketosis on a strict diet. Most people who are more than 10 pounds overweight should also avoid it.

• DR. COOPER'S FABULOUS FRUCTOSE DIET •

In order to understand this diet it is necessary to understand that, in order to utilize sugars in the body, the body needs insulin. When too much insulin is suddenly secreted, stimulated by a high sugar load, the blood sugar drops and we feel hungry again, even if we ate the sugar only two hours before.

Dr. Cooper tries to eliminate hunger on his calorie-deficient diet by adding a sugar which is, in effect, slowly released into the bloodstream from the intestines and gives a more even blood sugar level. This more even blood sugar level is less likely to stimulate an excess of secretion of insulin, and hence less likely to make you hungry even though you're on a low-calorie diet.

The diet itself is of the familiar high-protein, very-low-carbohydrates (some vegetables), low-fat variety.

Menus for a typical day on Cooper might be:

Breakfast:	2 eggs (fried or scrambled), 2 oz. lean pork
Lunch:	2 oz. beef liver fried in 1 teaspoon oil, and endive salad with 3 tablespoons permitted dressing
Mid-Afternoon:	Snack — 3 fructose tablets
Dinner:	4 oz. chicken (no skin) and green salad with 3 tablespoons permitted dressing

COMMENTS: This is essentially a real starvation diet (600-800 calories per day plus salads). The menus emphasize chicken and fish, which are lower in calories than beef. Dr. Cooper's fructose idea may work for you, and the fructose contribution to the diet's calories is negligible. He does specify quantities, and his diet seems easy to stay on for long stretches — he allows salads, and his diet is not quite as boring as some diets.

You can use fructose tablets with any diet, if you don't like Dr. Cooper's. My own opinion is that the fructose is a possibly helpful idea, and that the diet will help you lose weight rapidly in the beginning with or without the fructose.

However, like ketosis, fructose's reduction of hunger is a reduction of physiological hunger and as such may not suppress psychological hunger, except insofar as taking the fructose psychologically makes you think you will be less hungry. Furthermore, fructose reduces ketosis, which *may* be suppressing your hunger, in which case you may end up hungrier than you would be without the fructose.

The important thing about any diet, of course, is that you end up thin. I hope that at this point in the book you are armed to stay on any diet of your choosing, and I hope this chapter has helped give you an overview of some of the most popular diets. If none of them seems right for you, take heart—none of them was right for me, either. The one that *did* work for me—and works for so many of my patients—is described in the next chapter.

CHAPTER 15

MY
DIET

The diet on which I lost—and kept off—72 pounds takes weight off in a hurry, especially in the beginning. The diet averages out to a loss of about 3 pounds per week, but losses of 5 to 10 pounds for the first and sometimes the second week are common. The first time I went on it I lost 14 pounds in 14 days; recently, returning to the diet after a gain on vacation, I lost 6 pounds in three days.

Why such a quick and substantial loss? Is it water? Does the weight stay off?

The reason for the large and fast initial weight loss is linked to the fact that the diet is totally unbalanced. On diet days you eat *only* protein, no carbohydrates at all, and a tiny amount of fat. (Binge days are, of course, different.) Is the initial weight loss mostly water? No, why should it be? If you eat fewer calories than you need, your body burns fat.

My diet, although it is not the easiest diet in the world to stay on, is not by any means the most difficult, thanks to the quick rate of weight loss and the allowance of binges. It allows between 600 and 750 calories a day—few enough so that anyone who goes on it will lose weight very rapidly, about a pound a day for an initial period of time. How long this period lasts will vary from person to person. For example, if you're a carbohydrate junkie and you suddenly eat nothing but protein, you may lose 14 pounds in the first two weeks, which may be all you have to lose. Will it stay off? If you remain on the diet or on maintenance, of course it will stay off—and you can drink all the no-calorie liquids you want. Again, the loss is not water!

What about the rest of the weeks, or months, on the diet? Well, you know that you are entitled to a binge of 2,000 to 3,000 calories every 10 pounds, so the 2 or 3 pounds gained while binging will cut down your average loss quite a bit. But remember, we are not worried about time, we are worried about staying on a diet, for a long time if necessary, and using the diet to correct for binges while on the diet or while on maintenance. That's why it's important to be able to go off and on this diet at will, why binges are allowed—even encouraged—while you're dieting.

Those people who lose all their excess weight in two or three weeks on the diet must also learn to use it as a correction to binges on maintenance. This diet is particularly good in this respect—you can use it to lose two or three pounds in two or three days and return to maintenance. Let's stop, right now, worrying about how fast you can lose the weight—which really means worrying about how soon you can get off the diet. Don't forget, you can never get completely off some diet. Controlled binging is fun, but it's also a form of dieting. Maintenance is a diet. Anything that doesn't amount to total, out-of-control freedom—eating as much as we want as often as we want—psychologically to us fat-persons is a diet!

We're always going to be on some diet. Refusing to face that fact is why you have always gained your weight back in the past. The only time you can eat what you want for one or two days is when you plan—and limit—a deserved binge. The only time you can eat out of control for one or two days is when you're at your goal weight, have held that weight for some time, and *know* that at will you can go back on your diet and take the weight off. My diet will get you back to maintenance very rapidly.

Now for the diet.

Breakfast:	3 egg whites fried in 1 teaspoon oil, and 2 oz. 1% milkfat cottage cheese
	or
	1 egg (*no* oil or butter), with or without 2 oz. 1% milkfat cottage cheese
	or
	1 oz. hard cheese
Lunch:	3 oz. can tuna (packed in oil or water—see below)
	or
	5 oz. can white-meat chunk chicken
	or
	4 oz. fish, shellfish or chicken
	or
	1 frankfurter
Dinner:	4 oz. fish, fowl, or beef
Liquids:	Black coffee, tea, no-calorie soda, and water—as much as you like.

No vegetables, no fruits, no foods made with flour. You've seen it—if it's not listed above, don't eat it or drink it. No alcohol. That's it. Very simple. No complications.

The preparation of the food can be as simple—or as complicated—as you want it to be, within the limits of the diet. If you have a recipe that involves 18 exotic spices, three hours of preparation, and doesn't break the rules of the diet—fine. The suggestions that follow, however, will involve your spending very little time in food preparation. To me, that's a plus. Less time spent in the kitchen is less time spent with my mind on food.

Now, about the egg whites. At first you may find the very thought unpalatable. Well, if you've eaten fried eggs you've eaten egg white plain, only you also had the yolk. So now you don't have the yolk, but you do have cottage cheese. You'd be surprised at how good—and how substantial—the combination tastes. I break the egg so as to allow the yolk to stay in half the egg shell, let the white fall out, fry it well on both sides. Then I top it with cottage cheese.

When I don't need the cottage cheese (or am saving it for later in the day), I have used some fake syrup (no-calorie) on the egg whites on a Sunday morning, to pretend that I'm eating pancakes. The egg whites, with or without the cottage cheese, do help you—and your stomach—feel that you've got something for breakfast (and if you don't eat them in the morning you can make them once a day, any time). You're likely to be eating the three egg whites and 2 oz. of 1% milkfat cottage cheese together; the one egg can be eaten alone, and the cottage cheese can be saved for later. Notice that you cannot use oil if you eat the egg—the yolk has fat. You also can't eat tuna packed in oil if you eat the egg. If you have egg whites made without oil—in a nonstick pan—you *can* have tuna in oil.

As to the chunk white meat chicken, make sure the label on your brand doesn't list anything else but chicken, salt, broth, and preservatives. The tuna should be packed in water. But again, if you scramble your egg whites in a nonstick pan without the oil (I make them in a nonstick pan even when I do use the oil), then you can save your oil allotment for tuna packed in oil instead of water. Fifty calories of oil is 50 calories of oil. For that matter, you can skip the oil from the egg whites and instead put 1 teaspoon of butter on your fish (or whatever). If you really can't stand egg whites, or would like a change from them, have the 1 oz. of hard cheese instead. Just remember that this completely uses up your oil allotment.

So much for breakfast. What do you do with the rest of your mingy daily allotment of protein? When I grow weary of looking at a piece of fish, I squeeze lime—that's right, lime not lemon—all over it. The next night I might add up to two tablespoons of teriyaki or Worcestershire sauce, or V-8 juice (not calorie-free, but close to it). I have a friend who prefers to poach the piece of fish in V-8 or, sometimes, in dry white wine (the alcohol and calories in the wine boil away, and the fish is left moist and tasty), plus herbs or spices. I also use all the imitation butter *flavoring* I want.

The first thing I do with a piece of chicken is to remove the skin, which is where many of the calories are found. (The chicken, incidentally, can be white or dark meat. When you're talking about portions as small as the ones on this diet, the difference in calories between white and dark meat isn't a factor.) Many of the tips I've mentioned for making fish more appealing work equally well for chicken. I'm also fond of dried onion chips and garlic powder. If I pan-stew chicken in V-8, I either use little enough V-8 so that the increase in calories is negligible (3 ozs. has 17½ calories), or I use 6 oz. and compensate by cutting 35 calories' worth off the piece of chicken.

To me, the easiest "piece of protein" to deal with is a lump of chopped meat. It's not as unappetizing in its uncooked state as fish or chicken, and there are many things you can do to vary its taste. All of the additions listed above for spicing up chicken and fish taste fine with ground beef (except for lime juice and wine), and my favorite way of preparing hamburger is tasty enough to get it on the request list of non-dieters. I take a small, heavy skillet and cover the bottom with dried onion chips and garlic (to taste, and in any form except garlic *salt*). I heat the pan and add the hamburger. As the hamburger cooks, the onion chips cook in its fat. If the meat itself is very lean (ground round or sirloin), I don't worry about the small number of calories that will be added when I spoon what's left in the frying pan over the hamburger. If I've used ground chuck or plain ground beef, I pour off (or blot up with paper towels) as much of the fat as possible.

The same technique works fine with steak or veal. And the purpose of all these cooking tricks is the same — to add flavor and variety while adding virtually no calories. If you enjoy cooking, use your imagination and you can come up with plenty of tricks of your own.

When it comes to your fish, fowl, or beef, it doesn't matter whether you broil it, bake it, poach it, pan-fry it, or just breathe on it—so long as there are no fats (unless you've saved your 50-calorie teaspoon of oil from breakfast), no juices other than lime, lemon, or a little V-8, no sauces (other than Worcestershire, teriyaki, and Tabasco), etc. (spices are fine).

Do I really have to tell you any of this? You know how to diet, you know you have to weigh everything or measure everything. You know you can't put Hollandaise sauce on your fish. Nor can you have lobster with even a smidge of butter—unless you owe yourself 1 teaspoon of oil from breakfast. I wouldn't advise eating lobster if you can't enjoy it without butter. Cocktail sauce—*one* ounce—is allowed with 4 oz. of shrimp or crabmeat. Mustard is okay. Ketchup is out. Soy sauce, teriyaki sauce, Worcestershire sauce are okay up to 1 tablespoon; tabasco sauce is fine in whatever quantity your stomach lining can take.

In general, you can eat whatever you are allowed *whenever* you feel like eating it. You can have lunch for breakfast, or dinner for lunch—it doesn't matter. But be careful—if you use up 4 oz. of beef for lunch, you're obviously into a hungry day, and you'll have a hard time holding yourself to 4 oz. of fish for dinner when the time comes. Sometimes I know I'm going to have a long day; so I save my egg whites and cottage cheese for after dinner. Sometimes I deliberately (with great effort!) don't eat anything *all day* so that I can have 8 oz. of fish or chicken for dinner plus an egg or egg whites and 1% milkfat cottage cheese fried in 1 teaspoon oil. Notice that you can't have 8 oz. of beef for dinner, even if you starve all day—I'm sorry, but beef ounces have more calories than fish or chicken ounces. A beef entrée adds up to 800 calories and with the egg or cheese, you get a calorie total of around 900.

But I don't have to tell you to follow the diet the way it's laid out. You're an expert. I'd rather talk about energy and ketosis. Let's start with ketosis. This diet produces a severe degree of ketosis very rapidly; and *some* people may experience a sick or nauseous feeling at the beginning of the diet. If that happens, just eat either two lumps of sugar (two teaspoons) or one piece of white bread. You'll feel better in about a half-hour. If the nauseous feeling comes back later, eat another piece of bread. If you have it the next day, have some vegetables, anything from spinach to beets (one cupful), and that should do it. You will probably feel better by the following day and can resume the diet without these additions.

I don't experience this feeling of nausea, but every time I go on this diet for more than three days I get diarrhea, which lasts about two days and then settles into the usual diet constipation. If the diarrhea and ketosis-nausea hit at once you may think you're really sick or that you can't stay on this diet. Not so. Both will go away in one or two days. If you have diarrhea while on this diet and eat some vegetables—that's right, eat roughage—the diarrhea will nearly always go away. If you're sick for more than two days, see your doctor.

Most people, however, don't get sick. It has been my experience that for the most part the ones who do get sick on this diet are those who are trying to weigh less than their goal weight as determined by the formula for women (5 pounds per inch over 5 feet, plus 100 pounds), or for men (5 pounds per inch over 5 feet, plus 120 pounds).

You will remain in ketosis throughout this or any other high-protein, low-calorie diet; it's just that this diet produces a high degree of ketosis very rapidly. Get through the first three days, and you'll be on your way. After the first three days, although I was in ketosis for a very long stretch of time, I had no trouble. Neither have my patients.

Now to energy. You know, dieting produces psychological effects. As soon as we know we're on a diet, we feel drained of energy. Not because we are eating fewer calories, but because *we use up a tremendous amount of mental energy preventing ourselves from eating all day.* The only thing super-energetic about Dr. Atkin's super-energy diet is that it allows snacks of cheese or other protein-fat combinations that enable you to relax your vigilance. It isn't the calories in the cheese that makes the difference—we all have so many stored-up calories that a few external ones aren't going to raise our energy level. It is the "now-I-can-eat" reaction, the relaxation of our eternal control, that gives us the feeling that we have more energy. The measly piece of cheese does add a few milligrams to your blood sugar total, which might have the effect of giving you a slight lift— but I doubt it. The relaxation of vigilance several times a day is far more likely to give you an overall feeling of energy, or at least make you less tired, on the Atkins diet.

If this type of boost works for you, go ahead and break up lunch and dinner on my diet and save two 1-oz. pieces of fish or chicken or beef for snacks. My own opinion, however, is that psychologically it is a good thing to delay the gratification of your hunger—which you will have to do to maintain your weight loss—and not have snacks unless they are absolutely necessary to your staying on the diet. Drink no-calorie beverages whenever you feel hungry. They are surprisingly satisfying.

What if you feel that salads are absolutely necessary to your staying on this (or any) diet? I have one salad a week in a restaurant that serves the salad with real blue cheese crumbled on top; and a little (100 calories' worth) dressing underneath. I just can't eat salad without dressing, good dressing—not low-cal, ugly-tasting dressing. If you're like me and don't consider salad a salad unless it has a good oily dressing, then stay away from salads except for once a week. If you like low-calorie dressings (two teaspoons, please); if a quarter of a head of lettuce, a fourth of a cucumber, a little celery and green pepper turn you on and make it possible for you to stay on the diet, go ahead. Eating this type of salad every day won't hurt the diet, though it may slightly slow down your weight loss.

When it comes to other foods you feel you can't live without, my advice is to wait for your binge day. You'll enjoy eating the food all the more for having earned it.

And now to vitamins and minerals: there are two mineral supplements you need on this diet, and they must be taken religiously. They are calcium and potassium. Tums (the antacid) contains 500 mg. of calcium carbonate per tablet — most other antacids do not. Take two Tums every day. This calcium is essential because the diet is deficient in calcium.

As for potassium, your body loses it when you go on a high-protein, low-calorie unbalanced diet like this one. The body doesn't lose *all* its potassium, just enough so that you need 25 milliequivalents a day of potassium as a supplement. Potassium comes in tablets or effervescent pellets, and in this dosage will usually require a doctor's prescription. Now, potassium should not be taken by people with certain kidney problems, which is another reason why you should see a doctor before going on this or any diet.

All you need of any other minerals and trace elements can be found in standard over-the-counter multivitamins. For good measure, I would (and did) take two B-complex with C and minerals per day. The dosage isn't important, *standard* (as opposed to geriatric or stress formulas) over-the-counter multivitamins will suffice. If you *want* more supplementation than this, that's fine so long as you don't take more than two multivitamins a day if they contain iron. Check the label, also, for vitamin C, which is included in most multivitamin formulas. You need about 250 mg. per day.

If you take the vitamins and minerals listed here, you are, in effect, balancing the diet without adding the calories from the foods that contain the vitamins. When you use the diet for maintenance corrections, or stay on it less than one week for any reason, it's not necessary to take the potassium. More than one week and you need the potassium. The calcium should be taken whenever you use the diet.

The nicest part of this binge-and-starve diet is, of course, the binging. You can *and should* binge after every 10-pound loss unless you have only 10 pounds to lose—in which case you can either skip the binge or binge at minus 5 pounds. The binges should total 2,000 to 3,000 calories, depending on whether you're willing to add 2 or 3 pounds while binging. Here's an example of what you might order dining out for a 2,000-calorie binge (assuming you haven't eaten anything all day):

Salad with dressing: 200 calories

Steak (8 oz.): approximately 800 calories

Side order of spaghetti: 400 calories

Cheesecake: 400 calories

Coffee with cream: 100 calories

Miscellaneous: 100 calories (in case portions are not exact or in case you have a piece of bread)

Binge, starve, get thin—and stay thin. What more could you want from a diet?

CHAPTER 15

SUCCESS
AT
LAST

Let's prepare for a diet. I'm assuming that you have somewhat solved your unconscious reasons for staying fat and are reasonably "up" for a diet. The first thing to do is pick a date on which you intend to start the diet. The date should be at least one week away from the present date. Then, and this may sound strange, go on a binge. And I mean get it *all* in.

Why do I say binge when you are consciously up for a diet? Because I want to prepare you for deprivation. I want also to have you eat or binge without guilt. As soon as you hear the word "diet" you want to binge anyway, and the smartest thing to do right before the diet is to give in to that urge and go ahead and binge. This means, of course, that you'll be starting your diet a few pounds heavier than you would without the preparatory binge; but weight that goes on quickly may come off quickly, and in any case, the psychological advantage of the binge is too important to be missed.

Obviously, you must stop binging on the date you chose as D-day. If you are really up for a diet, the preparatory binge will not keep you from going on the diet at the proper date. If you think it will, maybe your unconscious reasons for being fat are still unconscious. With a binge-and-starve concept the binges are controlled—*exactly* what you are going to eat on the binge is *planned*—and the diet itself is a starvation diet of any type you choose, so long as you, or the diet, set the calorie total at fewer than 800 calories (preferably 600).

A 600-calorie diet will cause a loss of a pound a day for the first three or four days of the diet, and possibly longer. So, let's say you've starved for six days and you've lost 6 pounds. If you have to go off the diet, go off, gain 2 pounds, and go right back on. You have a net loss of 4 pounds, and who's going to sneeze at 4 pounds?

If you can continue to starve because it's so much fun to watch the weight drop off, do it. When you feel yourself in need of a binge and you've lost at least 10 pounds (except for 10-pound losers, who are better off binging at 5 pounds), and are confident in your ability to stay on the diet when you decide to stay on the diet, plan a binge for the next day or two. Write everything that you want on the binge down and have it. You can write whatever you want. You must decide and accept the fact that it will be a one-day binge, and that you may not eat after midnight on the binge day. If you do, you have unconsciously "ruined" the next day, and will use that as an excuse to eat the next day too.

Eat only what you have written down. You can eat less, but don't use that as an unconscious excuse to eat the rest of the week because you didn't finish your binge. Enjoy the binge. You've earned it. Go right back on your diet the next day.

Control is definitely the name of the game; and once you can plan and execute controlled binges, you've put the basic control concept into action.

The following steps, which summarize successful weight loss from beginning to end, are ones I have offered to my patients who prefer to have a plan of action spelled out for them. As you read them, you will see that every one of them involves *your* taking control of your eating.

1. Solve, or at least recognize, the unconscious determinants of your need to eat or need to be fat. Use the steps outlined on page 78, or any other method that works for you, but take steps to rob your unconscious of its power to keep you overweight.

2. Divorce food from its unconscious meanings—love, sex, power, rebellion—whatever meanings it has for you. Food is not love or sex, fat is not power, and so on.

3. Divorce food from emotions. Stop eating to assuage anxiety, depression, anger, or loneliness. Food doesn't really allay these feelings; it nearly always makes them worse.

4. Choose a diet that appeals to you (see Chapter 13).

5. Pick a date on which you will begin dieting, at least one week from the day you take this step.

6. Go on a two- or three-day binge, during which you eat anything you want, as much as you want. Get it all in. You'll gain some weight, but that's okay. If you're really ready to diet, if you have achieved Steps 1, 2, and 3, the extra weight won't be nearly as important a disadvantage as the advantages you'll get from having binged before you start depriving yourself.

7. Stop binging at 12:00 midnight on the day before D-day.

8. Stay on your chosen diet until you've lost 10 pounds. If you've absorbed what you've read in this book and you've followed steps 1–7, this time you'll be able to do it.

9. After you've lost 10 pounds, go on a planned one-day, 3,000-calorie binge. Follow the suggestions on page 162 in planning the binge.

10. The day after the binge, go right back on your chosen diet and stay on it until another 10 pounds have disappeared and you've earned another planned-binge day. Continue this binge-starve pattern until you've reached your goal weight.

11. Once at goal, choose a maintenance plan (see page 211) and stay on it for two to three weeks. If, while on maintenance, you find yourself gaining even slightly, reduce the calorie total

for your maintenance diet. If you find yourself losing, either binge yourself back up to goal or adjust the calorie total slightly upward.

12. After two to three weeks of holding your weight on a maintenance diet, go on a 2,000–3,000 calorie, planned one-day binge.

13. The day after your binge, go back to your weight-losing diet until you've lost any weight gained from the binge.

14. Now that you're back at goal weight, continue to follow a maintenance diet interrupted every few weeks by a planned binge, followed by a short diet, followed by a return to maintenance, and so on.

• FOOD FOR FANTASY •

There are very weak moments in dieting. They happen to all of us almost every day. They happen especially when we are waiting for, say, a bus or train. It's so easy to grab a candy bar at the station. The first thing we think of, when we have nothing to do, when we don't want to do anything, or when we have a little time to kill, is food. I have found that consciously making myself think of all the rewards of thinness is of great value in weak moments.

Force yourself to think about what it would be like to be thin. I think first of not having to sit with my arms across my midriff to cover the fat roll there. Men and women can stop wearing jackets in the summer or give up the eternal raincoat. What about bathing suits? Picture yourself, if you can, in a bikini, whether you are male or female. No stomach hanging over or out. How about being about to wear blouses *in*, without a jacket? How about making love without self-consciousness? Picture looking in a mirror naked and liking it. Think about being able to buy whatever you want in a clothing store because nothing makes you look fat.

So far, we've talked about looks, but the new feelings about yourself are almost indescribable. If you get thin and stay thin, there is a feeling of having won, having won what may well be the biggest battle of your life. All losses in life can seem small compared to this, the big win. What's more, other challenges become easier, thanks to your increased self-confidence. You feel that "If I can lose weight, I can do anything."

Our feelings about ourselves do depend, to a certain extent, on the way other people feel about us. There is no question that other people, mates, children, job staff, store owners, and so on, treat us differently when we're thin. This difference really amounts to respect—respect for our having won the battle. You will feel this respect from them and you will have respect for yourself, a respect that is difficult to imagine even in fantasy; but it will be there for you when you lose weight.

Everything will seem better. Even long-standing problems will seem more solvable when you get thin. You will be more in control, not only of yourself but of other people and situations.

This even holds true on the romance front, for singles of any age as well as marrieds. When you lose weight, you can afford to be choosy, and you can even afford to be rejected. Yes, afford to be rejected, because you won't feel that he or she who rejected you is the only man or woman you could get. This also goes for marrieds. They can afford, mentally, socially, and emotionally, to get a divorce, if that's what they want.

At any rate, these are just some fantasies. Think about your own, whatever they are. Think about how getting thin will affect your life. Do this often, and particularly when you feel you're going to cheat on your diet.

• STOPPING YOURSELF •

There are feelings in our pre-conscious minds which, if we think about them, may be on-the-spot reasons for eating. We don't ordinarily think of them; all we feel like is eating. These feelings form a mnemonic HALT, which you can think about whenever you get the urge to eat. H stands for Hurt, A for Angry, L for Lonely, and T for Tired.

There is no question that we fat-persons eat when we get hurt. Often we get hurt and cannot stand up for ourselves. We are afraid of being further rejected if we protest the original rejection. Often, we get hurt about being fat. What can you say about that? The instinct is to eat, but food will not really assuage the feeling of being hurt. It only makes the hurt worse, and it will certainly make you feel guilty. Don't eat—HALT!

Anger is a big one. Many of us swallow our anger, literally, with food. We don't think about being angry, just about eating. How can you tell if you're angry when you're about to eat? It's simple—you are always angry at yourself for being fat, and that anger is easy to get in touch with. Think about what has happened in the past 24 hours. You may be angry about something that happened a day ago or more. If you can remember a situation or a remark that made you feel hurt, is it possible that it made you angry as well? Think particularly about remarks made by people close to you, especially, but not necessarily, around the issue of weight. It may not even be a remark. If your husband is serving the potatoes and gives you less, especially if you haven't said you were on a diet, you feel hurt because, just by that gesture, he is indicating both that he's aware of your fatness and that he wants you to do something about it. This is cause for hurt feelings, but also for anger ("Why can't I be accepted for myself and why can't I control what I eat?"). The idea is to think before you grab that piece of food. HALT!

Hurt and anger often take the form of unhappiness or depression. Before you eat, think "Am I unhappy or depressed? Will food make it better? Why am I unhappy? What has happened or been said to make me unhappy or depressed? Is my period coming on? Have I got problems with the children? Am I depressed about being fat? Yes, always, but is something else depressing me? Do I need love or attention or affection or sex? Are those things food?" My advice is to try to go and get what you really want. Don't substitute food for it.

Loneliness often drives us to eat—good old "food-is-love". Loneliness often involves boredom and lack of intellectual stimulation and emotional support. If you have no friends or lovers, whether this is a result of being fat or the reason why you became fat, food won't help you now. Food is not emotional support. If you want to eat and realize you're really lonely, you can turn to people instead of food, or you can try to do something intellectually stimulating. You can take up a sport like swimming or tennis, fat as you are. The point is to do something to alleviate boredom and understimulation. Food won't do it. HALT!

Tiredness is the biggest danger to us all. Our will power absolutely breaks down when we are tired. Solution: get out of the kitchen. If you're tired, go lie down, don't hang around food. Think before you eat. Will overeating solve the problem of being tired? No, it won't. What it will do is saddle you with the problems of guilt and rage against yourself which will in the end further exhaust you. HALT!

Think: Hurt Angry Lonely Tired—HALT. Thinking "Halt" can stop you from eating. Ask yourself if you are in any of these states when you are about to cheat. Food will not help any one of them and will make you feel worse about yourself.

Incidentally, the concept of HALT was borrowed from Alcoholics Anonymous, but it is equally applicable to us fat-persons.

●   MAINTENANCE   ●

If you've followed the suggestions in this book, you have achieved the first goal of successful dieting. You have lost weight; and what's more important than the pounds you've lost is the confidence you've gained in your ability to control your own weight.

Successful dieting, of course, is not just a matter of taking weight off. The ability to *keep* it off is the crucial hallmark of successful dieting. Staying thin involves your continuing ability to control your own weight, which brings us to maintenance.

What, exactly, is maintenance? Maintenance is a diet, let's face that right at the outset. If you can't eat everything you want, you're "dieting," right? Right. Does this mean you're going to be on a diet, most of the time, for the rest of your life? Yes, it does. That is the price of thinness for us fat-persons. If you truly want to stay thin, you will forever be maintaining, binging, dieting, maintaining. Even on maintenance, however, you can plan a binge, or succumb to an unplanned binge, and then go back on whatever diet works for you, losing the two or three binge-gained pounds and resuming your diet.

Did you think that once you were thin enough to be concerned about maintenance, you would stay that way forever? Of course you didn't—you know, from bitter experience, that there's nothing automatic about keeping weight off. Your loss is threatened by entertaining, by parties, by eating out, by pizza being ordered in, by all unplanned overeating (binging). Again, you *can* go back on your diet, lose the weight from the binge, and return to maintenance.

What, exactly, is a maintenance diet? What is the "proper amount" of maintenance calories? No matter what other books tell you, in caloric terms it is pretty close to 10 calories per pound of goal weight for women, and about 15 calories per pound of goal weight for men, plus or minus 200 calories, depending on how active you are. In other words, for a woman who now is at goal at 125 pounds, the maintenance calorie total is about 1,250 calories per day. She can probably get away with 1,450 if she is very active, but if she is sedentary, she may only be able to eat as few as 1,000 calories per day.

Naturally, the more exercise you do and the more running around you do, the more calories you can tolerate without gaining weight. Many books go as high as 15, 20, or 25 calories per pound for maintenance — 25 calories per pound for highly active people, particularly men. I have found that 25 calories per pound, even for men, is much too high, that no originally fat person can maintain his or her weight at 25 calories per pound, unless he or she happens to be a manual laborer.

Men who lead a sedentary life also require about 15 calories per pound to maintain. For some men, even this may be too much. The way to be sure, male or female, is to keep a record. Figure out how many calories you need, based on 10 calories per pound of goal weight for women and 15 calories per pound of goal weight for men, and then try to include some foods in your maintenance record that you want. Keep a record of what you eat each day and total up the calories in each day's eating. See how much weight you gain.

If you do not gain any weight, then average out the calories per day. The total is what you're allowed as a regular maintenance diet. If you do gain weight, go back on the starvation diet for a couple of days, lose the weight, and start again on an attempted maintenance program. This time moderate the calories even more. You may, for instance, be able to eat only one fattening thing that you like per day. I'm sorry, but that's maintenance.

A typical 1,250-calorie maintenance diet might be:

Breakfast:	2 eggs (fried in 50 calories' worth, or ½ tablespoon, of butter, equaling 250 calories if the eggs are large — no toast) and 8 oz. of orange juice (adding another 110 calories)
Lunch:	5 oz. chicken (trimmed of fat) or tuna (water-packed) and no-cal soda, iced tea, black coffee (and you've added only another 200 calories)

Dinner: (the big meal) 5 oz. beef or 8 oz. chicken or fish (300 calories), salad with dressing (150–200 calories, depending on the dressing) and nothing else except non-caloric liquids

I'm sorry, but as you can see from the above, it *is* a diet. If you don't want to regain the weight you fought so hard to lose, you can't stop dieting except when you plan a binge.

But take heart! Remember that if you can solve the unconscious problems that work to keep you fat, and if you've divorced food from its unconscious meanings, then that knowledge, plus the confidence gained from successful weight loss, enables you to diet, binge, diet, and maintain with a lot less feeling of deprivation and even some fun.

Does all of this mean that you'll either be on a starvation diet or a maintenance diet or a one-day binge for the rest of your life? If you're a true fat-person, you probably will.

Remember, though, that the very fact that it's maintenance you're concerned about means that you've reached your goal weight. With the loss of those unwanted pounds, you've gained not only a slim figure, but something even more important — the knowledge that you can have control of your weight for the rest of your life.

Binge, starve, maintain — and love that control. Love your thin self!

APPENDIX 1

Generic Name	Brand	Company

● ANTIANXIETY (CHEMICAL ANXIETY) AGENTS ●

Phenothiazines

Generic Name	Brand	Company
Acepromazine	Notensil, Plegicil	Clin-Byla
Acetophenazine	Tindal	Schering
Butaperazine	Repoise	Robins
Carphenazine	Proketazine	Wyeth
Chlorpromazine	Thorazine	Smith, Kline & French
Dixyrazine	Esucos	Union Chimiques Belge
Fluphenazine	Prolixin, Permitil	Squibb, White
Mepazine	Pacatal	Warner
Mesoridazine	Serentil	Sandoz
Methophenazine	Frenelon	Medimpex
Methotrimeprazine	Veractil, Levoprome, Nirvan	May & Baker, Lederle, United Drug
Methoxypromazine	Tentone	Lederle
Perphenazine	Trilafon	Schering

Generic Name	Brand	Company
Phenothiazines (continued)		
Pipamazine	Mornidine	Searle
Piperacetazine	Quide	Pitman-Moore
Prochlorperazine	Compázine	Smith, Kline & French
Promazine	Sparine	Wyeth
Promethazine	Phenergan	Wyeth
Propericiazine	Neuleptil	Rhone-Poulenc
Propiomazine	Largon	Wyeth
Prothipendyl	Timovan	Ayerst
Thiazinamium	Multergan	Rhone-Poulenc
Thiethylperazine	Torecan	Sandoz
Thiopropazate	Dartal	Searle
Thioproperazine	Majeptil	Rhone-Poulenc
Thioridazine	Mellaril	Sandoz
Trifluoperazine	Stelazine	Smith, Kline & French
Triflupromazine	Vesprin	Squibb
Butyrophenones		
Dehydrobenzperidol	Innovar	McNeil
Haloperidol	Serenace, Haldol	Searle, McNeil
Thioxanthenes		
Chlorprothixene	Taractan, Solatran	Roche, Warner
Clopenthixol	Sordinol	Ayerst
Thiothixene	Navane	Pfizer
Xanthiol	Daxid	Pfizer
Reserpines		
Deserpidine	Harmonyl	Abbott
Rescinnamine	Moderil	Pfizer
Reserpine	Serpasil and others	Ciba and others

APPENDIX 2

Generic Name	Brand	Company

●   ANTIDEPRESSANTS   ●

Tricyclics

Generic Name	Brand	Company
Amitriptyline	Elavil	Merck
Desipramine	Pertofrane, Norpramin	USV Pharmaceutical Geigy, Lakeside
Imipramine	Tofranil	Geigy
Nortriptyline	Aventyl	Lilly
Protriptyline	Vivactil	Merck
Trimipramine	Surmontil	Rhone-Poulenc

MAO Inhibitors

Generic Name	Brand	Company
Etryptamine	Monase (withdrawn)	Upjohn
Iproniazid	Marsilid (withdrawn)	Roche
Isocarboxazid	Marplan	Roche
Mebanazine	Actomol	Imperial Chemical Industry
Pargyline	Eutonyl	Abbott

Generic Name	Brand	Company
MAO Inhibitors (continued)		
Phenelzine	Nardil	Warner
Pheniprazine	Catron (withdrawn)	Lakeside
Tranylcypromine	Parnate	Smith, Kline & French
Prescribable Stimulants		
Amphetamine	Benzedrine	Smith, Kline & French
Dextro-Amphetamine	Dexedrine	Smith, Kline & French
Deanol	Deaner	Riker
Methamphetamine	Desoxyn	Abbott
Methylphenidate	Ritalin	Ciba

● NONBARBITURATE MINOR TRANQUILIZERS
AND SEDATIVES ●

Chlordiazepoxide	Librium	Roche
Chlormethazanone	Trancopal	Sterling-Winthrop
Diazepam	Valium	Roche
Hydroxyzine	Vistaril, Atarax	Pfizer, Roerig
Meprobamate	Miltown, Equanil	Wallace, Wyeth
Oxazepam	Serax	Wyeth

BIBLIOGRAPHY

Atkins, Robert C.: *Dr. Atkins' Diet Revolution*. New York: Bantam Books, 1977.

Atkins, Robert C.: *Dr. Atkins' Super-Energy Diet*. New York: Bantam Books, 1977.

Cooper, James T.: *Dr. Cooper's Fabulous Fructose Diet*. New York: M. Evans and Co., 1979.

Fredericks, Carlton: *High-Fiber Way to Total Health*. New York: Pocket Books, 1976.

Kraus, Barbara: *Calories and Carbohydrates*. New York: New American Library, 1975.

Nidetch, Jean: *Weight Watchers Cook Book*. Hearthside Press, 1966.

Stillman, Irwin M.: *Dr. Stillman's 14-Day Shape Up Program*. New York: Dell, 1974.

Tarnower, Herman: *The Complete Scarsdale Medical Diet*. Ramson Wade, 1978.